THE HORMONE DIARIES

THE Bloody Truth ABOUT OUR PERIODS

First published in Great Britain in 2019 by Wren & Rook

ISBN: 978 1 5263 6146 2
E-book ISBN: 978 1 5263 6156 1
10 9 8 7 6 5 4 3 2 1

MIX
Paper from
responsible sources
FSC® C104740

Wren & Rook
An imprint of
Hachette Children's Group
Part of Hodder & Stoughton
Carmelite House
50 Victoria Embankment
London EC4Y 0DZ

An Hachette UK Company
www.hachette.co.uk
www.hachettechildrens.co.uk

Publishing Director: Debbie Foy
Senior Editor: Liza Miller
Art Director: Laura Hambleton

Designed by Thy Bui
Medical consultant: Dr Max Pemberton

Printed in the United Kingdom

Additional images supplied by Shutterstock

HANNAH WITTON

THE HORMONE DIARIES

THE BLOODY TRUTH ABOUT OUR PERIODS

wren
&rook

Contents

Introduction

Talking about our bodies, getting to know how we physically function and sharing our experiences is more important than ever. Like it or not, despite the hard work of feminists and movements celebrating body positivity, we are still shrouded by taboos and stigma concerning our bodies.

But one of the biggest body taboos – still – is something we don't tend to see in our visual culture: menstruation, a.k.a. your period, Aunt Flo, shark week, that time of the month. Whatever you call them, periods are a natural part of life. We often think of them as annoying inconveniences – they're painful, messy and make us sad or angry – and in some cultures they're even seen as an illness. But the fact is, periods are a sign of a healthy functioning body and they're not going away any time soon. So we may as well do ourselves a favour and get period positive.

In 2016, having been on the pill for seven years, I decided to come off it. There wasn't anything wrong with the pill I was on, it worked fine. I just missed my periods. That's right, I MISSED MY PERIODS. Nothing to worry about, the pill I was on had a very common and normal side effect of lightening, reducing or completely stopping periods. But still, I was 24 years old and I hadn't had a period since I was 17. Seven years! I started to wonder if my period would ever come back, along with the rollercoaster of emotions, the mood swings and urges that I'd once known always accompanied it. Being on the pill usually keeps PMS (**prem**enstrual **s**yndrome) at bay – it stabilises these emotions. On a practical level, that was great – but I was starting to forget who pre-pill Hannah was. Was I experiencing the world as I 'should' be? Was it easier – but also flatter and duller?

You hear all sorts about how the pill can affect hormonal balance. That it can impact your mental health, how you feel about yourself and how you feel about others. It's hard to know what's true – there might be cases where all of these things have happened as a result of the pill. Or they might just be spooky tales we tell each other. Either way, a lot can change in seven years, and 24-year-old me was a very different person to 17-year-old me. So I wanted to find out the truth. Was I the same person off contraception as I was on it?

This is when my YouTube series *The Hormone Diaries* was born. There I documented any changes to my mind, body and soul from coming off the pill, sharing my experiences as I researched other options. Amongst other delights, I've made videos about my screwed-up 'monthly' cycle, trying a menstrual cup for the first time, and the highs and lows of having sex on your period. Going on hormonal contraception often isn't about sex – loads of people get it to help with periods and puberty symptoms before they're sexually active. This book is for readers aged 15+ – so while you may be under the age of consent in the country where you live, that doesn't mean that conversations about hormonal contraception aren't important for you. Especially because when you're a teenager, you tend to just go on the first pill your doctor recommends, no questions asked – and if the side effects aren't nightmarish, you stick with that one without exploring other options. But as you get older, you start learning that there are other types of viable contraception out there. Maybe your pill has stopped serving you in the same way it used to, or maybe you've read scary news articles about some potential side effects.

It felt like my friends and I all had this realisation around the same time. How much did we really know about the contraception we were using – and was there another type out there that would be better for us? How do these hormone regulators we've been taking work in our bodies? Why should we settle for an unsettling list of side effects just to not get pregnant when condoms exist? We want our quality of life to be as good as it can be, don't we? And most of all, we don't want to have to worry and think about it all so much.

Just think, what could we be doing if we weren't so preoccupied with having a uterus? Reflect on the amount of time you've spent dealing with PMS, researching ways to make it better, cleaning yourself up after starting your period unexpectedly, the amount of money spent of period products, the amount of time thinking about your contraception, talking about it (with friends and with health professionals), researching your different options, going to appointments, going to the chemist, reading a book about it, writing a whole bloody book about it. What else could we achieve in that time?

But this book is not just about periods and birth control. We will talk about them, lots, but *The Hormone Diaries* is so much more than that. It has come to be about all things contraception, periods and bodies. In the YouTube series I have made videos about HRT (hormone replacement therapy and disorders like PCOS. We're going to cover all that and then some in this book.

This book is for everyone who wants to learn about periods, whether they have them or not. After all, not all women menstruate (trans women don't, and cis women may not either, because of the contraception they're on, or other health reasons) and not all people who have periods are women (AFAB non-binary and trans folks).

No book is perfect, but I want to be as inclusive of trans and non-binary people as possible. However, I may use the word 'women' sometimes because it's this area of so-called 'women's health' – often inadequate,

AFAB means 'assigned female at birth', and in this book I'll be talking about AFAB people most of the time, whether cisgender, non-binary or trans. You might have guessed, but AMAB means 'assigned male at birth'.

underfunded and straight-up ignored – that has got us into this hot mess of being confused about our bodies.

Since I started *The Hormone Diaries*, more and more friends of mine have been sacking off the pill. But this isn't a book trying to persuade you to try a non-hormonal contraceptive life. Absolutely not. Everyone is different – whilst coming off hormonal contraception may work for some, I want to stress how bloody amazing it is in the first place, and how lucky we are to have it (even with all the side effects). And in fact, I spend a lot of this book trying *not* to persuade you in either direction – for two reasons. First, I am not a doctor! I'm fascinated by this stuff and I've done lots of research but I am not medically qualified at all. Secondly, what feels right for one person is totally different to what feels right for another – it's all about choice, not my personal recommendations. We're figuring this out together.

My favourite thing about doing *The Hormone Diaries* on YouTube has been the comment section. It's not something you hear a lot of internet creators say, but the comments on those videos are always so thoughtful and interesting. People from all different countries, ages and genders share their experiences with these topics and I soon realised that I wanted to document that somehow. So I asked my amazing audience to share their own hormone diaries in the style of letters, and you're going to see some of them in this book. I had hundreds and hundreds of responses (thank you so much!) and I couldn't include them all, but I hope you find some comfort that you're not alone from the ones I've featured. You might even be inspired to write some diary entries of your own – you'd be amazed at how cathartic it is.

I hope this book answers some questions you might have, fuels your curiosity, makes you feel a bit more normal and gives you the confidence and knowledge to question whether your period products and birth control are right for you. And if they're not, to arm you with courage to explore other options and, most importantly, to speak to a doctor if anything doesn't feel right.

The information contained in this book is not intended to replace the services of trained medical professionals or to be a substitute for medical advice. You are advised to consult a doctor on any matters relating to your health, and in particular on any matters that may require diagnosis or medical attention.

WAIT — WHAT ARE HORMONES?!

Hormones are chemicals that travel around our bodies causing cells or tissue to act in a certain way. They control most of our bodily functions. When we say, 'I'm feeling so hormonal' in relation to PMS, we're only referring to one or two of many different hormones that are created in glands all over our bodies. These control things such as sleep, stress, hunger, blood sugar levels, calorie-burning, heart rate, growth and sexual urges. You may have heard of cortisol, a.k.a. the stress hormone, or melatonin, a.k.a the sleep hormone. Hormones rule over our body via the endocrine system and a doctor who has specialised in hormones is called an endocrinologist.

But don't worry, this is not an endocrinology book – we're only concerned with a few hormones: oestrogen, progesterone and testosterone, the sex hormones! Ovaries produce all three while the testes only produce testosterone. They impact our lives in various ways. Oestrogen is one cause of puberty (bringing you greatest hits including periods, hips and boobs) and prepares the body for pregnancy and regulates the menstrual cycle. Progesterone also helps out with the menstrual cycle and pregnancy. And testosterone is another cause of puberty (taking a bow for facial hair, increased bone density, muscle mass and strength). As this book is the bloody truth about our periods, we're going to be mostly talking about our dear friends oestrogen and progesterone.

WHERE IT ALL STARTS: PUBERTY

Puberty is the process in which, through physical changes caused by hormones, a child's body becomes an 'adult' body that is capable of reproduction. I say 'adult', but in fact you could be done and dusted with puberty at 13 years old. Puberty is when our hormone journey – something we may spend our whole lives trying to understand – really begins. It can be a wild ride: the anticipation, the shock, the am-I-normal? questions – all swirling around the fact that our bodies are technically now preparing for reproduction.

I'm not going to lie: for me, puberty feels like for ever ago. My boobs came in towards the end of primary school, so out with the vests and in with the crop tops. I no longer just had nipples, I had BOOBS! I specifically remember the tissue around my right nipple swelling up first; I would poke it thinking, *Is this it?* I ran into the bathroom where my mum was having a bath to show her my one boob and asked if I was growing breasts. I'll always be very grateful for the relaxed atmosphere in my house which meant I could barge in on my mum's bath time and feel normal about flashing her my nips.

By stark contrast, a few more years into puberty, I was lying in the bath and this time it's Mum who barges in. She points at my crotch and makes a comment about my baby pubic hair and I screamed at her to get out. I was absolutely mortified. And that's what puberty did for me; I went from not caring about my family seeing me naked, and not caring about seeing them naked, to being so self-conscious of my body. Covering everything up and making sure no one could see. As puberty advanced, so did my shame. And I wasn't the only one.

Even in secondary school, I don't remember seeing any naked boobs in the girls' changing room. Many girls, including myself, wore sports bras, and we had mastered the art of changing bras under T-shirts without flashing our boobs. Ingenious, right? If only there'd been a GCSE for pretending our boobs and pubes didn't exist. Most of us adapted and learned to get comfortable with our changing bodies in time – for me, having parents who are open and relaxed definitely helped. But periods, they were another level. If I was self-conscious about my burgeoning boobs, I felt completely isolated when my periods started.

I was just about to turn twelve when I got my first period – while watching *Freaky Friday* at the cinema with my friend and both our mums. Nipping to the cinema toilets, there it was: blood staring right up at me from my knickers. What did I do? I stuffed my pants full of toilet roll to soak it up, and when we got home I told my mum, who was extremely prepared. Even though I was just 11 years old and my sister was nine, Mum had a supply of tampons and pads at the ready.

I didn't tell anyone else, though, not for two years. I was convinced that no one I knew had started their periods, and I didn't want to be the freak who started early. I *wanted* to tell my friends – keeping it a secret was hard work, as well as an emotional burden – but I had no idea how to bring it up. How was I supposed to just *slip it into* the conversation? But, just like with the onset of boobs and pubes, I found out I wasn't the only one going through it. Hanging around at my friend's house after school when we were thirteen, she casually grabbed a tampon out of a drawer, waved it at me and went off to the bathroom. And just like that, the spell had been lifted. It turned out that most of my friends were getting visits from Aunt Flo, too. If only I'd asked! All that time wasted on being embarrassed. See, talking about things is always better than keeping them bottled up inside.

This is where my personal period adventure takes on a quirk all of its own, and where my experience of puberty isn't like most people's. I had something called ulcerative colitis, or UC – a form of inflammatory bowel disease, which would affect me with flare-ups. When this happened, I would take medication and the UC would eventually go in to remission. During secondary school, I had flare-ups aged 12, 14 and 15, and during those times my periods stopped. It's common for your periods to be a bit irregular when you first get them, but usually they settle down. But mine never did. The UC flare-ups would disrupt my cycle too much. This was both a blessing and a curse. My cycles were usually very long, maybe five or six weeks between each period instead of the common four weeks, which was great – less time bleeding! Less PMS! Fewer tampons and pads! But it also meant I never knew when my period was going to start. I don't remember having any clear PMS symptoms in advance that would give me the heads-up, so they always came as a surprise. The stop-starts continued until, before they got a chance to regulate naturally, I went on the pill at 17. Since my very first period during *Freaky Friday* to when I came off the pill at 24, I'd spent more years not having periods than having them.

What was the natural period experience like? I wondered. Not only did I want to find that out, my fascination with periods – what they're for, what they affect, what comes with them, and how to make them work for us better – led me to create *The Hormone Diaries*, and to build the online community that became part of my period exploration. Between us, we got to grips with all the issues around menstruation and shared our stories.

PART ONE

Periods

Most of us will spend around 40 years having periods – from our early teens to our early fifties. That's a LONG time to experience monthly bleeding, mood swings, (sometimes crippling) pain, bloating, heightened sensitivity and the lack of confidence that comes with skin break outs and water retention. Oh yeah, we love to complain about periods – but I think we're allowed to!

Not only can periods alter the way we think and feel about ourselves and our bodies, they influence the rest of our lives too. They affect our relationships with friends, family and partners. They drain our finances thanks to expensive period paraphernalia. And our periods, and the PMS symptoms that come with them, can dictate our ability to do what we like each day, from taking part in our favourite hobbies and sport to going to work. The fact is, periods have the potential to wreak havoc in almost all aspects of our lives, so we owe it to ourselves to understand a bit more about them.

HERE COMES THE BLOOD

First things first, let's have a quick recap.

What is a period?

Your period is part of the menstrual cycle. During your cycle, the lining of your uterus thickens in preparation for a fertilised egg to nestle in, get comfy and grow a baby. Roughly halfway through your cycle you ovulate, which is when an egg pops out of one of the ovaries and into a fallopian tube. It sticks around for about a day waiting to get fertilised by any potential sperm kicking about, and then gets on its merry way down the tube towards the uterus.

This is when it all starts to sound like science fiction. A fertilised egg is called a *zygote* and the cells inside multiply as it travels down the fallopian tube towards the uterus. By the time it reaches the uterus, it's no longer a *zygote*, it's a *blastocyst*, and this is what attaches itself to the uterine lining in a process called implantation (told you, science fiction). The uterine lining has grown thick in preparation for the egg. But if there's no sperm just chilling up inside your reproductive system, an unfertilised egg comes passing through and leaves your body along with the discarded uterine lining. This is your menstrual period. The day you start your period is day one of your menstrual cycle.

People can get concerned about whether their periods are normal, and the good news is, they probably are. Period blood can be all shades of red and brown, slippery, sticky, mucus-y, clotty, bloody. There can be lots of it or just small amounts of it. It might smell a bit or it might not smell much at all. Everyone's period will be different and your period may even change characteristics from cycle to cycle – it's all normal! (Unless your period is blue like the liquid in tampon and pad adverts – that's not normal, you should really see someone about that.)

Dear light periods,

Thank you. Thank you so much for blessing me these past few years. After having experienced heavy periods for more than a decade, I feel so blessed to have light ones now. You have been amazing and I sincerely hope you stick around.

Best wishes,
Beth, Belgium

Dear vagina,

Please stop bleeding like a waterfall every month. And please stop making my whole back hurt for two days straight.

Thank you,
Frida, Sweden

The floodgates open

The Curse, surfing the crimson wave, code red ... The reason periods are talked about in code is because they're somehow meant to be embarrassing and shameful. There is still a huge amount of stigma surrounding periods. But what benefits are there to shaming and making jokes about a perfectly normal bodily function? Anyone would think that people who have periods should feel apologetic about something that is biologically out of their control and is natural and important. We're not supposed to talk about periods – especially not around men (God forbid!) – and we're certainly not allowed to visually represent them either. Photos of period blood on bed sheets get flagged and deleted from Instagram. That's right – a normal bodily function gets censored because other people find it 'gross'.

I want to put the idea that periods are gross to bed once and for all. Since we're the ones pulling out tampons and menstrual cups full of blood, changing soggy pads and cleaning stains from underwear and bedsheets, we could do without the extra shaming. If you don't have periods but you like to tell us how gross they are, perhaps being face to face with a menstrual cup full of period blood would shut you up. Periods involve blood – that doesn't automatically make them gross. Most of the time we're not even complaining about our periods because of the blood, but because of all the add-ons like PMS or frustrating period products. But some people do experience an extremely heavy flow – not so much a wave more a crashing tsunami. I've never experienced the latter, but a friend of mine recently described her overflow to me: her tampon soaked up so much blood that it started to come down the string and she had to use two pads as backup. Turns out, this isn't unusual – just not something I'd personally ever experienced.

That is why I wanted to include your stories. I'm just one person, one body, one experience. And there are so many others out there!

Dear my period,

Why, oh God why, did you pick the week before my A2 Level exams to have abnormal excessive bleeding? Usually, I'd have loved an excuse to avoid taking countless mock exams and doing continuous past-paper essays (hello medieval history A Level), but not so close!

As if realising something was wrong when at a friend's house party wasn't stressful enough

(I LOVED discreetly cleaning up their bathroom floor), ending up in hospital in need of a blood transfusion was the icing on the cake.

This amount of bleeding during your period, making a blood transfusion necessary, is very rare. According to the NHS, most menstruating people will lose less than 80 ml of blood during their period. If you're curious, you can measure how much you bleed by using a menstrual cup, but don't worry if you can't be bothered. Most people know what a normal amount of bleeding is for them.

I suppose I had ample time lying in bed waiting for a few pints of blood to go into my system to go over my revision flashcards, but there is only so much reading about the Magna Carta a dizzy girl can do. And even then, the TV on the ward was showing Piranha 3-D which wasn't exactly my first choice.

So thank you, periods, for shedding enough blood to warrant a hospital trip, and for my reluctant introduction to the Piranha franchise. Thank you for ensuring I get judgy looks when refusing to donate blood to the NHS (I'M SORRY but I'm not allowed to post-transfusion).At least it got me started on the pill, which has both blessings and curses …

See you soon,
Alex, UK

P.S. I haven't had another freak incident since and am 100 per cent fine.

If you can, please give blood! It's so important. I can't because of my UC, but when I had surgery, I needed two bags of blood. Do it, do it!

How to remove blood stains from clothes and bedding

All you'll need is cold water, salt and lemon juice. Squeeze lemon juice on the affected area, then scrub the stained area with salt. Without rinsing it, soak it in cold water for at least thirty minutes (a few hours or overnight is best though). I once bled all over a white and blue top after a blood test – my vein just wouldn't stop! But overnight in a cold salt water concoction and all the blood was gone.

So, back to my personal experiment. What actually happened to my period when I came off the pill? Did my period return? Well, yes it did, but it took its damn time about it. I had to wait about six weeks after coming off the pill for my period to finally turn up. I was carrying around stashes of tampons and pads along with my menstrual cup (maybe slightly overboard) every day during that time, waiting for it to arrive, never really knowing because my PMS symptoms weren't that predictable or accurate ...

When it finally did happen, of course I was at a fancy-dress party wearing a really short white dress and white knickers.

After that, I had periods for about a year. Many times I was convinced I could feel my period in my pants, but it was just sweat or discharge; other times I literally felt the moment it started, the very first blob of blood dropping out of my vagina. Bodies can be unpredictable like that.

Dear my irregular periods,

Why are you so irregular? I've been having periods for almost nine years, and even though there have been times you've been reasonably regular, why can't you just settle down? This summer, it was nice not having you whilst on holiday, but a three-month gap between periods?! For once, it would be nice to know when you're likely to arrive — to be able to plan, to be able to relax in the knowledge there's nothing wrong with my body. Every time there's a worryingly long time between periods, you just happen to come in the next few days.

WHY?!?!

Hannah, UK

Here's how my periods played out during that year:

Day One
Heavy bleeding and intense cramps. A hot-water bottle, loose comfy clothes and painkillers were all very necessary.

Day Two
Still heavy but a bit less bleeding. Dull cramps. Could usually get through the day without painkillers.

Day Three
Medium bleeding.

Day Four
Light bleeding.

Day Five
Slightly lighter bleeding.

Day Six
Very light bleeding.

Day Seven
A light dribble.

You might be wondering why I only had my period again for a year. Long story short, I went back on contraception – more on that in the next chapter.

Dear my period,

I wonder if you'll ever come back. Perhaps this is it for us. If I can trick my body into stopping you, then I'm all for it. You weren't even that bad compared to some stories I've heard. It was mostly the boob pain that forced me back on hormonal contraception. But you, you were fine. I just didn't like some of your friends.

Hannah
x

I missed my period!

Your first thought might be that missed period equals pregnancy – and whilst that can certainly be true, there are a few other explanations for amenorrhea (the medical term for periods stopping in our reproductive years). The average cycle is 28 days, ranging from 21 to 40. I don't think I've ever had a regular cycle in my life so I'm not sure I can say I've ever 'missed' a period, because I never know when it's going to show up in the first place. But for varying reasons, my periods sometimes have stopped for a while. So here are a few reasons you might miss your period other than being pregnant – some of these could also be reasons why, if you're in your late teens or twenties, you haven't started your period at all:

1. Weight gain/weight loss – if you lose or gain an excessive amount of weight over a short period of time this can mess with your cycle and cause your periods to stop.

2. Stress – your mental health can affect all sorts of other things in your body. If you lose your period during a time of stress, your body might be sending you a sign to look after your brain.

3. Over-exercising – as well as putting your brain under a lot of stress, putting your body under stress can also stop your periods. It's why so many atheletes have amenorrhea.

4. Chronic illness – your overall health can have an impact on your menstrual cycle. Whenever I've had flare-ups of my ulcerative colitis, my periods have stopped. It's like my body is saying, 'One thing at a time, please!'

5. PCOS – this stands for Polycystic Ovary Syndrome. PCOS is a condition that can disrupt your periods, leading them to be irregular.

6. Hormonal contraception – some kinds of hormonal contraception (progestogen-only pill/coil/implant/injection) may make your periods lighter, less frequent or stop them completely.

7. Menopause – menopause is when your oestrogen levels drop and your periods stop for good, usually around the age of fifty. Your periods can also be unpredictable during the years leading up to menopause, a time known as perimenopause.

The guidance offered by the NHS is that if you've missed three periods (not had a period in three months) and pregnancy tests are coming back negative, you should go to your doctor to see if there may be something else affecting your menstrual cycle. And of course, go to the doctor if you are actually pregnant.

PM-SODDING-S

PMS, my friend, **premenstrual syndrome**. Characterised by boob aches, mood swings, back pain, acne and headaches – to name just a few of its delights. What is PMS?

Premenstrual syndrome is the name for the symptoms that can occur a week or two before your period. Most people who have periods experience PMS to some degree – there are many different symptoms, there can be different intensities and PMS may affect you differently throughout different stages of your life. The symptoms can be physical, emotional or behavioural.

Here's a list of the most common ones:

breast tenderness

MOOD SWINGS

HEADACHES

back pain

CRAMPS

ACNE

BLOATING

weight gain/loss

feeling anxious, irritable or upset

changes in appetite or food cravings

CHANGES IN SEXUAL URGES

TIREDNESS

That's quite a lot of symptoms. And this is all *before* you actually start your period – fun! Though for some people, the symptoms might continue throughout the bleeding. When I was writing this book, one of the first questions that popped into my mind about PMS was *why*? I know why we have periods – because our bodies are preparing us for pregnancies that don't then materialise. But why all the symptoms beforehand? I optimistically and naively thought that a quick internet search would answer my question. But I should have known better. Because this is women's health we're talking about. And if there's anything I've learned from making *The Hormone Diaries* video series, it's that we still know very little about why our bodies work the way they do. The NHS website simply says,

'It's not fully understood why women experience PMS.'

Great.

It goes on to say that, 'it may be because of changes in your hormone levels during the menstrual cycle.'

What I take from this is that biology is punishing us for not getting pregnant. Egg comes out to play, doesn't get fertilised, your body is sad and throws a temper tantrum for a week or so until you bleed it out.

Obviously, this is just my silly hypothesis. Remember, 'it is not fully understood why women experience PMS.' Also, it's possible to experience PMS whilst fertile.

It's evolution's way of encouraging us to procreate. I mean, don't we have ENOUGH dodgy messaging from society about whether or not we should have children? Do we really need our own bodies chiming in with physical and mental discomfort?!

One horrendous symptom of PMS, which I myself have experienced, is ...

Boob pain

Dear my boobs,

Why do you hurt for two solid weeks before I get my period?!
What have I done to deserve this?
Why do you hurt so much?!
Everything would be fine
and then one day I'd take
my bra off in the evening ...
and instead of gently flopping
down into place, you'd
plummet with all of gravity's
force that you could muster.
It was like you were getting
denser and denser all day in the
bra without telling me, and when I took my bra off, you thought it
was this funny practical joke. But I screamed in pain and had to
try and grab my boobs to stop the fall hurting so much. And that's
how it would go for two weeks.

This may have something to do with the fact that oestrogen makes breast ducts enlarge and progesterone makes milk glands swell. When hormone levels change, pain and soreness in the breasts can result.

I couldn't receive big hugs because anything pressing against you was agony. You felt ten times heavier than before. Sexy boob time was off the table because it hurt too much.

No matter how long my cycle was, the pain stayed for two weeks. You're lucky I didn't have a regular 28-day cycle or I might have gotten you chopped off.

You are the reason I had to go back on hormonal contraception. I hope you're happy.

Lots of love,

Hannah
x

Cramps

Other than my excruciating breast pain, the only other PMS symptom I really experienced was cramps. And I consider myself very lucky that my cramps were manageable and only lasted two days max. Nothing some painkillers, a hot-water bottle and lying down wouldn't fix. But cramps for some can be completely debilitating and, depending on the severity, impact their ability to do normal daily activities. Even with my moderately painful cramps, sometimes I would have to lay on the sofa with a hot-water bottle under blankets and work on my laptop from there – I don't know what I would have done if I needed to go into an office or attend meetings. *Sorry I can't come in today, I've got*

PMS. It sounds like a joke, but for some people it really can be that bad.

> Dear period cramps,
>
> I am writing this huddled up to a hot-water bottle trying to block you out. You've brought along your friends lower back pain, nausea and hormonal acne. As house guests go, you are definitely not perfect. I want you to leave almost immediately and have to do extra shopping to prepare for your arrival (although that is conveniently predictable, so thanks for that I guess).
>
> Waiting patiently for you to leave until next month.
>
> Laura, UK

Acne

Acne is not a joke. It is the one symptom of PMS that is properly visible and the effect it has on self-esteem cannot be underestimated. I am grateful to have escaped it, but for so many people, it is part and parcel of the glorious PMS experience. Another crappy thing to deal with. If you are one of thousands who suffer from acne or hormone-related skin conditions, don't let shame make you suffer in silence. Talk to your doctor about what you can do to reduce or even eliminate it – and find the best option for you.

(Not so) dear acne,

I went on my first pill to stop you from happening so much. At the time, I thought this was mainly a good excuse to start birth control. Fortunately for you, this first pill didn't do very well, Even more fortunately for you, the second pill I tried made my skin look even worse! Third time's the charm, however, and you (kind of) went away for a while.

But during this whole ordeal I had also figured out that I wasn't really going to need the pill for any other reason besides your presence. Because I am actually a huge lesbian. So, once I realised that, I thought being on the pill just for you was a bit drastic. So I quit and you came back with a vengeance. After a few months of being fairly miserable, I decided to start the pill again. You went away but it left me feeling uncomfortable about all the hormones I was putting in my body just to deal with you. I actually found a really great face cream recently that helps me even more than the pill does, so I quit the pill again. This time, hopefully for good.

See you never, acne,
Kaloe, Netherlands

Mood swings

Mood swings are not fun for us and they're not much fun for other people. The peaks and troughs of emotions during PMS are not helped by our ingrained conditioning that certain emotions are negative. Sadness for example. How many times have you been told to 'cheer up'? First of all, there is nothing unnatural about feeling angry or weepy or short-tempered. Stop apologising for it. But do explain to those you unleash your emotions on that you have PMS. The good news is that the mood swings will pass. When you feel them coming on, do something tried and tested to soothe you: listen to music, watch good TV, spend time with people who have a calming influence on you. Avoid those triggers that heighten your emotions. Look after yourself at this time. You're not alone and you're still fabulous.

Oh, and if you are grumpy without being on your period, don't let people mutter something about PMS. Enough of that shit. We are allowed to not be 100 per cent happy 100 per cent of the time.

Dear preconceptions,

Why must you assume I'm on my period because I'm grumpy or upset? Believe it or not, not every woman gets PMS and I'm guessing the majority of us are NOT in fact on our period when you accuse us of being on it.

Sabrina, Nicaragua

PMDD (Premenstrual Dysphoric Disorder)

Most people who have periods will experience mild to moderate PMS symptoms. But those struggling with more severe cases have their own category – Premenstrual Dysphoric Disorder, or PMDD. PMDD is not something me or my friends were taught about in school – it was something I became aware of in my twenties, only because I was seeking out this information.

PMDD affects about 5 per cent of people who have periods. Simply put, the symptoms of PMDD are a more severe and debilitating version of the symptoms of PMS, and they include depression and suicidal thoughts. Like PMS, the symptoms of PMDD may come for a week or two before your period and then get better.

I am not a doctor – you knew that already, but I feel like I need to state that again here. I can't diagnose anyone. But if you suspect you have PMDD and it is severely hampering your day-to-day life and affecting your relationships or your ability to do normal daily tasks, then do go see a doctor because there are ways to treat PMDD.

I think one of the reasons we don't hear much about PMDD or give sufferers permission to seek help is because we don't take women's pain seriously. It's just a natural burden we're supposed to bear for being women. It's been reported that there is a pain bias in the medical industry. It's unclear if it's due to a gender bias in medical staff, lack of research on women or differences between how men and women interpret and communicate pain. There are also emerging theories about racial bias – that black women's pain is ignored more than white women's pain. One thing's for sure, there is a clear difference in how men and women are regarded and treated when it comes to pain. So if you're in lots of pain, speak up. Pester your GP about it, ask for a second opinion, ask for a referral. The pain is real and should be treated properly.

Dear PMDD,

When you first appeared, I thought my severe depressive mood that lasted two weeks each month was just a part of being moody before my cycle. I ignored you, because you were not taken seriously enough by society and shrugged off as a normal part of a woman's life. Your symptoms were sometimes seen as comical and general thinking that women should just put up with being 'emotional' or 'moody' every month.

But you weren't just a comical 'mood swing', or just a 'her time of the month'. I realised that my condition was serious. I wasn't going to put up with you or let society think you were just an unimportant mood symptom of my period. This was not normal and I shouldn't have had to live with you every month.

After consulting my GP and naturopath, I carefully listened to a diagnosis of PMDD and the various treatments available. I was inspired to treat you naturally, even if it would take many months — I was not interested in using the pill to mask my symptoms.

Having been very patient and persistent with treatment, four cycles later you have left me. Gradually after each cycle I felt a gentle shift in my mood until you faded. I'm grateful that my symptoms of you were not so severe that I was able to take it slow and treat you naturally over time, as I imagine sometimes you are not so kind to others.

Goodbye PMDD, from a girl you torment no longer.

Ella, Australia

Coping with PMS

It's not all doom and gloom! For most people, PMS is pretty mild. But here are some tips and tricks on how to best deal with the symptoms. If you're in a serious amount of PMS-related pain or emotional discomfort, though, do go to your doctor.

Exercise

This may seem like the last thing you want to do, but the endorphins released from exercising are a natural painkiller and exercise can help lift your mood. The idea of hitting the gym might be too much, so maybe try something low-impact such as swimming, going for a walk or yoga.

Painkillers

Paracetamol or ibuprofen will do. Don't bother with the extra-expensive ones that say they're specifically for periods. That's just branding and all painkillers are made up of the same stuff.

Stress management

Whatever that looks like for you, find time to do yoga, read a book, have a bath, meditate and so on.

Go to sleep

I'm a big sleep advocate for everyone all of the time, but getting your full eight hours can especially help during PMS.

Track your period

Use period-tracking apps to monitor your symptoms and get to know your body. It can be easier to prepare for and treat symptoms if there's a pattern you recognise.

Birth control

Hormonal contraception can change your PMS (for better or worse).

As well as these ways to help ease the physical and mental symptoms of PMS, you may find you also need to manage relationships around it – with friends, family and partners or with teachers, colleagues and bosses. If you are aware of your PMS and you know roughly when which symptoms will occur, talk to the people in your life who are best supporting you and are there for you with chocolate, hugs and the food you love. If you need to be alone, then let those people know.

We've been conditioned to believe that PMS isn't a serious thing and it's often the butt of jokes, but if your PMS impacts your work or studies then it *is* serious, so talk to your teacher or your boss. You won't be perpetuating the stereotype that women on their period are weak and useless, absolutely not! You are more than capable, but letting people in your school or workplace know what's going on means they can adjust to help you during your PMS. You tell work and school when you're not feeling well in any other capacity, so don't feel bad about telling them about this too. It's a health issue and should be treated as such.

Track your cycle!

One recent development in the fem-tech world is period-tracking apps. For a lot of people, these have revolutionised their period experience. Many apps not only give you the option to track when you come on your period, but also when you have cramps, breast pain or changes in libido, as well as things like the consistency of your discharge. You can track almost everything to do with your body and cycle.

Bear in mind that I'm only talking about apps that track your cycle. These are used for knowledge and awareness, *not* contraception. Contraceptive apps are a whole other beast and we'll get on to those later.

A period-tracking app is a great tool to use when you go to your doctor about any symptoms you're having that concern you. It shows you all this useful data, and your phone has a record of the last time you had each of your PMS symptoms. The reason I know that my boobs started hurting two weeks before my period arrived was because I tracked it. When I saw those little dots on the screen, I could spot a glaringly obvious pattern. So even though my actual cycle was irregular – anything from 22 days to 52 days (but mostly in the 40s) – I roughly knew when I was going to start my period because my tits would start aching and, two weeks later, BAM. PERIOD.

Dear my body,

WHY IS IT A THING YOU DO TO GIVE ME CRAMPS
BEFORE AND DURING MY PERIOD?! There is no
need. Also boob pain. WHY IS THAT A THING? I'm
fifteen and (for a fifteen-year-old) I have
big boobs. It's already something that can
hurt my back, so why give me extra pain when
my body is bleeding. Headache too. WHAT is the
point. Why, just why?

I use a period-tracking app and I think it
might be one of the best things ever because
it's so accurate and really does help. I can
see what symptoms are consistent before,
during and after my period like BOOB PAIN
(really no need for it).

Lots of love,
Ellie, UK

PSSST — YOU DON'T HAVE TO GET YOUR PERIOD

I've talked about how *The Hormone Diaries* came about in the first place because I wanted to experience my period again. Well, I got my period again and realised that I much preferred life without it. Now here's the thing: you don't actually have to have your period if you don't want to or if your PMS or PMDD make it unbearable. Since the 1960s there has been a way to avoid periods (and also to have sex and not be pregnant all the time). Hormonal contraception! It is a very normal side effect of progestogen-only contraception, for example, for you to experience reduced periods or none at all.

Dear anyone considering the pill,

My periods were the worst thing ever (a lot of blood every day of my period, horrific cramps, nausea, dizziness, constipation ... not to mention the serious mood swings the week before!), but then I started taking the pill. I've been on it for six months now and there's no bleeding and barely any pain.

I was anti-hormones for so long, but the pill turned out to be a lifesaver for me.

Ellen, Belgium

There's a lot of talk about what's 'natural' for our bodies when striking the balance between periods and contraception. Having periods every month may seem 'natural' but it's actually not as simple as that. And I don't just mean when it comes to the pill. If we're talking about history, the 'natural' pattern of life for women was starting your period, finding a mate, then getting pregnant and breastfeeding – which got rinsed and repeated until menopause. With so many pregnancies, you wouldn't actually have that many periods. So who's to say a lifetime of monthly periods is 'natural' anyway?

Praise be that we're no longer completely beholden to our biology. Medicinal and cultural shifts mean we are in control of if, when and how we want to have children. But it does mean we have significantly more periods in our lifetime than our ancestors did, because, on average, we're starting our periods earlier, having children later and having fewer of them. It's no wonder that we're starting to think that a few fewer periods would be a blessing.

But would we be doing something wrong to our bodies by reducing or stopping our periods? Should we all free-bleed from now until for ever? How much should we want to experience our body's 'natural' processes even if we dislike it?

A lot of the thinking around what's 'natural' has a historical root. It's recently come to light that the week off the combined pill, which leads to a 'withdrawal bleed', is completely unnecessary (and potentially riskier, pregnancy-wise). There were a number of reasons why the seven-day bleed was originally recommended, one of them being to appease the Catholic Church. One of the inventors of the pill was Catholic – he thought the pill would be better received by his religion if women had one week off per month from taking the contraceptive medicine (even if the women were still protected from pregnancy during that week). Obviously, this news is pretty infuriating, especially in the context of the history (and present) of the Catholic Church intervening in women's reproductive health and choices. However, like most things, the story is more complicated and nuanced than the headlines have suggested – we'll go into it more when we talk about the dark history of the pill. But the point is, you don't have to have your period if you *don't* want to, and NHS guidelines have recently been updated to reflect that – see the next part of the book for more info about that.

I talk a lot about this with my friends. Ultimately, the choice is up to you. How important is having a period to you? Do you care if you don't bleed as long as you don't have cramps? Do you want to track your body's natural cycle? Do you hate your period so much that you'll do anything to stop it? That's your decision to make – I can't make it for you.

Dear period,

Can I keep you away for the rest of my life? In theory, yes – but you never know what's going to happen next. I can just put you off until I'm ready for babies and then experience you for however long it takes for me to get pregnant and then you'll go away again. I have all the power, I get to decide if, when and how you taunt me. And that feels good. You have so much power over the people you visit – sometimes you can ruin their day, week or even month. But not me. I've found something that works, and I won't let you disrupt it. Until I want you to.

Yours hopefully never again,

WHICH PERIOD PRODUCTS SHOULD YOU USE?

```
Dear menstrual blood,

Thank you for ruining my favourite jeans.

Much love,
Isabel, UK
```

With all the bleeding we're doing, we need something to stop it from staining our clothes and sheets or dribbling down our legs. And there really is something out there for everyone – to match your flow, your wallet, ethics and whatever feels comfortable. If you're unhappy with whichever period products you're currently using, maybe now is the time to try out something new. If not, then 'if it ain't broke, don't fix it'. Don't add further complication to your life.

Here is what is available to you:

Disposable pads

Worn in your knickers, a pad is sticky on one side to attach to your underwear and is absorbent on the other side.

Tampons

Inserted into the vagina, a tampon expands as it soaks up menstrual blood. You then pull it out with a string.

Menstrual cup

A menstrual cup made of silicone, it goes inside the vagina and collects menstrual blood. It is reusable – the cup is taken out, emptied, rinsed and reinserted.

Reusable pads

Cloth pads come in different colours, patterns and designs, and are used like disposable pads – but you can wash them afterwards to use again.

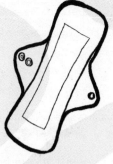

Period underwear

This underwear looks normal, but has an absorbent layer built in to catch menstrual blood. You wash it before using it again.

Each one of the above period products come in different shapes, sizes and colours. There are also multiple brands making each of them, so if you fancy giving a new product a go, you may wish to do a bit of research and look up reviews online first. This is especially worth doing if you're planning on getting any of the reusable products, because they can cost more upfront.

The cost of having periods

Here's where I'm going to get preachy. British women spend on average £4,800 in their lifetime on their periods and that is atrocious. These are necessary products for us to go about our daily lives, but they are so expensive – it's no surprise that lots of people can't afford them. We hear about other countries where people on their periods are kept hidden at home because it's seen as unhygienic – but there is a version of that happening in the UK too. Being unable to afford period products means that many young people are staying at home and missing school during their period. It can have a detrimental effect on a young person's future aspirations, confidence, mental health and relationships. Not only are they having to battle the stigma around periods, but also the added stigma and shame around poverty too.

Thankfully, there are lots of initiatives out there to help bring period products to those unable to afford them. As part of the End Period Poverty campaign, the pad manufacturer Always donated 16 million pads to girls in schools across the UK. Then there are organisations and campaigns such as Free Periods, The Red Box Project and Bloody Good Period donating period products, and Bloody Good Period do amazing work providing period supplies to asylum seekers and refugees. Obviously, donation drives are really helpful and get the necessary products to those who desperately need them. But to truly end period poverty, we'd need to end poverty – and no amount of donations can do that. It would take some serious government action. That doesn't mean I don't have hope. It's just going to take a lot of hard work, and we all need to recognise that periods aren't just personal – they're political.

If you can afford period products but are looking for the most cost-effective solution, reusable products are the way to go. Over the long run, they should help you avoid that massive £4,800 price tag. But ultimately it sucks in the first place that many period products add up to so much.

Disposable pads

Pads are easy, non-intrusive and they work. Stick them in your knickers and you're good to go. You can get them in different sizes and shapes depending on how heavy or light your period is – some people find their flow is heavier at night, for example. They can come with 'wings' that wrap around your pants to protect yourself from any side leaks. Pads are especially good when you first start your periods, because they can seem less daunting than inserting a tampon or a cup. However, for some exercise, like swimming, you may want to consider a cup or a tampon instead. Some people also find them uncomfortable and smelly, and since they're only one-use, there are repercussions for the environment and your finances.

Check your pad when you go to the toilet in case it needs changing, but you'll probably be able to tell without looking; if it feels heavier, it's time to change. For those with very light flow, a panty liner may suffice.

Dear pads,

Thank you for being. I know a lot of people diss you and they don't like you as much as tampons or menstrual cups or anything, but you are the best for me and you deserve to be loved. Except when you're leaking – I like you less when that happens.

Dóri, Hungary

> *Dear pads,*
>
> *Why are you so uncomfortable? You feel like I am wearing a diaper, and no matter how often I change you, I always get as sore as a baboon's ass. Hopefully I have found the love of my life, the menstrual cup.*
>
> *Pads, don't wait for me because I won't be coming back. This is goodbye.*
>
> *Carolina, Mexico*

Tampons

As a teenager, I mostly used a mixture of tampons and pads. On days when I was doing exercise, tampons were ideal because once they're inside, you can't feel them at all. Along with menstrual cups, they're ideal for swimming. Tampons are available in different sizes that relate to how much blood they can absorb before you need to change them. They can also come with or without applicators, depending on which you find easier to insert. The applicator is a cardboard or plastic tube that helps you push the tampon inside you and which you then dispose of. Without an applicator, you just use your finger. Maybe try both, and work out what you find easiest to use.

You can leave tampons in for up to eight hours and you pull them out from the string that dangles outside of your body.

As you get to know your body, you'll probably become aware yourself when it's time to change your tampon.

If you know you sleep longer than eight hours, it's probably best not to wear a tampon overnight because it increases your risk of toxic shock syndrome, or TSS; a rare but life-threatening condition caused by bacteria infiltrating the bloodstream through fibres in tampons and releasing harmful toxins. Symptoms include a sudden high fever, vomiting, diarrhoea, a red rash and dizziness. Try not to worry too much – like I said, it is *rare*. Just make sure you change your tampon regularly and use one with the lowest absorbency suitable for you.

Your wallet and the environment may take issue with tampons, and I'm going to 'fess up to something here: from the ages of 11 to 17, I flushed used tampons down the toilet. I wasn't aware at the time that you weren't supposed to do this; I knew that packaging and pads went in the bin but didn't realise the rules also applied to bloody tampons. Oceans, I am so sorry.

Dear tampons,

We have crossed paths before. Like when my friends offered you to me in high school or when my mom didn't get a chance to go shopping and asked me to grab some tampons for her on the way home. Like when my friend fainted because of you and I had to remove you from her vagina. You have literally been inside me *(further than any guy or girl has ever been), but still we don't get on very well. Tampons, you are like coffee to me. I like the idea of you, but I just can't get myself to like you. I'm sorry but I think we just aren't meant for each other. But that's okay. You will find other girls who will have no problem with inserting you, and I'll just stick to my pads (pun intended).*

XOXO,
Emilia, Poland

Menstrual cups

The period product the environment loves! You may not have heard of menstrual cups before because they don't get advertised as much as disposable products do. Since just one product can last you many years, menstrual cup companies don't get as much income and they tend to have small marketing budgets. So instead of TV ads featuring cups full of blue liquid, word mostly gets spread through recommendations from menstrual cup users – sometimes they even put stickers up in toilet stalls!

Menstrual cups are soft, silicone cups that are inserted in the vagina to collect blood, like a tiny bucket. When the cup is full, you remove it by holding a little stem at the bottom and pulling it out. Cups are reusable, so you only really need one (two at a real push if you want different sizes for different amounts of flow). They're more expensive to buy than a pack of pads or tampons (about £20), but one will last you up to 10 years, so in the long run you save a lot of money. Most high street chemists sell them now, but there are lots of different brands that you can also buy online.

Using a cup can be trickier than using tampons or pads at first, but it gets much easier with practice. Just make sure your nails are filed down before using one. Ouch. Here's my fun guide to using a menstrual cup:

Putting it in:

1. Wash your hands and then wash the cup in warm water.

2. Drop your pants and squat over or sit on the toilet.

3. Fold the menstrual cup in half or pinch it down on one side to make a cone-ish shape.

4. Gently push it inside your vagina.

5. Make sure the cup has 'popped' open, creating a seal.

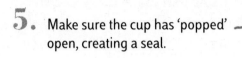

6. Run your finger around the edge of the cup to make sure it's open and sealed.

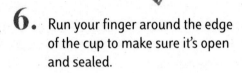

7. If it hasn't created a seal, you can adjust it a little with your finger or by pulling on the stem slightly.

8. The menstrual cup sits lower than a tampon does inside you, but everything including the stem should be inside.

9. Wash your hands and you're done! You can leave it in for up to 12 hours.

Taking it out:

1. Pull on the stem to bring the cup down so you can reach its base.

2. Slide your finger and thumb inside your vagina and pinch the cup.

3. Pull it out – use your pelvic floor muscles to push if you're struggling – and tip the contents in the toilet (nerd alert – before you do, you can have a look at how many millilitres you bled using the measuring lines on the cup!)

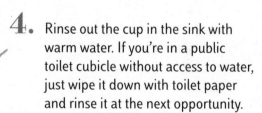

4. Rinse out the cup in the sink with warm water. If you're in a public toilet cubicle without access to water, just wipe it down with toilet paper and rinse it at the next opportunity.

5. Stick it back in.

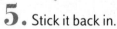

6. If it's the end of your cycle, rinse it then place it in a pan of boiling water for three minutes to disinfect. Dry it and store it in the little bag it came in, ready for next month!

Dear menstrual cup,

WHY MUST YOU HAVE INDUSTRIAL-STRENGTH SUCTION?

Sincerely,
Every woman who has been in the bathroom for
half an hour pinching the base to no avail.
(and also Shannon, UK)

According to research from 2015 on people who have periods, 24 per cent only use tampons, 31 per cent just use pads, 39 per cent use a mixture of pads and tampons, and 6 per cent use a menstrual cup. Come on people! It revolutionises the game! I will fully admit that I am a menstrual cup superfan. It literally changed my life. However, we're all different, and what works for one person might not work at all for another. It's your body, and your decision.

Dear menstrual cup,

It's not an exaggeration to say that you
completely changed my relationship with my
period and my hormones/menstrual cycle in
general. I used to view my period as an awful
burden that ruined my life every month and

forced me to create environment-destroying waste (in the form of tampons and pads) that I loathed, and it even made me resent being female. But once I mastered using you, my dear cup (it took a while!), my views on my period improved dramatically.

I no longer dread my period or resent my body, and so much of my mental health and self-image has been improved. I also love how convenient you are – no need to remember to carry tampons in every bag, purse and backpack – and how environmentally friendly you are.

So environmentally friendly!
One cup for ten years as opposed to 21 tampons or pads per period.

I can't put into words how much better you have made my life.

Thank you!
Danielle, Germany

Reusable pads

Reusable pads, also known as cloth pads. Where to start? Like cups, they're good for the environment. There are lots of different ones out there (or you can make your own). As well as big companies making them, you can find shops on Etsy of crafty people making and selling their own cloth-pad designs. And they come in amazing colours and patterns! I personally think it's worth trying them just for that. Search 'cloth pads' on Etsy and there are thousands of results, including, to my surprise, one with Donald Trump's face on it. Wow.

They come in different materials, shapes and sizes to fit your body, your underwear and your flow. Some come with wings, with little poppers to fasten underneath, and I've even seen ones specifically designed to be worn with thongs! I've never tried cloth pads personally, only because by the time I learned about their existence, I already had a good system going. But basically, they work in exactly the same way as disposable pads, except you can wash them and reuse them!

From what I've learned, everyone has their own way of cleaning cloth pads, so I would recommend reading a few blogs or watching YouTube videos where people explain how they clean and store their cloth pads. You can then play around with different methods and see what suits you best. You may need to alter your method slightly if you're staying away from home or travelling. But here are the basics:

1.

Have some kind of storage system for used pads (in your bathroom and your bag for days out/travelling). This could be a wet bag, mesh bag or plastic bucket, whatever you fancy.

2.

When changing a pad, fold up and snap the dirty pad shut and put it in your wet bag.

3.

Make sure your clean, dry pads are stored separately in a different place or different compartment in the wet bag.

4.

At the end of your cycle/
when the bag is full/when
you run out of pads, it's
time to wash them!

5.

For lightly used pads, you
can stick them straight in
the wash with your other
bits and bobs along with
the wet bag.

6.

For more soaked pads,
you can pre-rinse them in
cold water before adding
to your wash.

7.

Hang them up to dry!

There are other simple methods. Some people rinse them on the
floor of the shower whilst showering, handwash them, or leave
them soaking overnight in a bucket.

Dear my cloth pads,

Thank you for finally entering my life last year. I've longed for you since I was 14 and my older sister showed me that you existed, but my mother was not convinced and so I never got to have you. That is until last year, at 22, when I finally got to take the plunge and use you for an entire period. I didn't realize how much you could help my vulva from such disposable irritation, and my hormone and pH balance from being messed with by toxic chemicals making my periods so heavy and painful. And not only do you help with all of that, but no more embarrassing ripping sounds echoing throughout the bathroom when my disposable pads needed changing. No more having pads that were too short so I always had leaks. No more blue dyes and itchy plastic.

You are so soft and cutely shaped with so many fun patterns to choose from. I now own a pad that is 16 inches long for overnights and lovely 4–6 inch pads for daily liners and everything in between! HOW HAVE I NOT DREAMED YOU UP? YOU ARE A MIRACLE! NO – YOU ARE JUST FABRIC USED IN THE MOST PRACTICAL WAY! Gah!

All the love from my body, mind, and soul,
Katelyn, USA

p.s. Even cleaning you is easy!

Period underwear

This really is the future: underwear with built-in absorbency to soak up your period. I have a couple of pairs and they're just nice black, normal-looking knickers with a built-in pad. They come in all different styles and different absorbencies for light or heavy days. You can get briefs, thongs, high-waisted, boxers – whatever your style. The shorts/boxer style you can get is a great option for trans men who may feel dysphoric about using female-gendered period products.

The beautiful thing about period underwear is that you can chuck them straight in the wash, especially on light-flow days. If you're using them on heavier days – when you can visibly see the blood on the underwear – you can use the same method as cloth pads in terms of storing and rinsing them.

They're great for the environment but maybe not as great for your wallet. Period underwear is not cheap, so it may be unlikely you can afford to use them for your whole period – perhaps start with one or two pairs and then slowly build from there.

Dear period underwear,

BLESS YOU. THANK YOU. Where have you been all my life?! Why did I pay so much money for tampons and pads and bloodied underwear when I could have had you all along? I feel comfortable and safe. You brilliant underwear, you. Thank you for soaking the seeming gallons of blood that pour from my body away from me and my clothes.

An adoring fan,
Susie, New Zealand

We all have our go-to period products that work for us even if we sometimes have issues with them. But they help us out a huge amount, so here's to the wonderful product/s that stop us bleeding all over our clothes and legs.

PERIOD SEX: THE LAST TABOO?

There is a huge stigma around having sex on your period – and a myth that it's dirty and gross. In life, in movies and on TV, how many times have you heard, 'we couldn't have sex because I was on my period'? And when I asked people to write their own hormone diaries, though I got a huge response on the subjects of periods and sex, there was little to none on 'period sex'. Is period sex the last taboo?

If you're over the age of consent, the truth is you CAN have sex when you're having a period, IF you want to.

Let's break it down. Some people might not be into period sex at all, for all kinds of reasons, and that's absolutely fine. Maybe your period puts you in a very unsexy mood; you've only just started being sexually active and you've got enough to think about without adding blood into the mix; you're bloating, you're in pain and the last thing you want right now is to have sex. I feel you. Totally fine and you should always feel comfortable to say no to a partner whether you're on your period or not. But if you want to have sex on your period, talk about it with your partner, even if you're worried about bringing it up. If it is important to you, then it is important you are heard in your relationship. Don't assume that your partner won't be in to it.

First of all, let's define 'sex'. For our purposes here, it's any sexual genital activity, so that includes masturbation. Yes, you can also masturbate when you're on your period!

Why sex or masturbation during your period can be good:

You (and your partner/s) want to have sex and you ain't gonna let no period stop you

You may feel hornier on your period

Period blood acts as a natural lubricant

Orgasms/pleasure can help alleviate cramps

It's not as messy as you think and easy to clean up

It's normal, healthy and safe – lots of people do it (although this isn't a reason you should do anything – peer pressure is bad, so make the decision yourself!)

Here are some top tips for getting down whilst on your period:

Get a towel or consider having sex in the shower.

You may feel more comfortable getting down on the lighter days of your period.

There doesn't need to be any penetration! Use a tampon or menstrual cup and focus on the clitoris instead.

You can do whatever type of sex you like in whatever position, but missionary will probably produce the least amount of mess (because gravity).

If you want to, use menstrual discs – they are disposable, one-use-only barriers to stop period blood getting involved during sex (bear in mind they are not menstrual cups and they are not contraception!).

Use a condom! First of all, you can still get pregnant if you have sex on your period, so use protection. But also, a condom can help reduce the amount of mess.

Shower afterwards if necessary.

Clean any blood stains with cold water and salt.

What?!? You can still get pregnant on your period?!

Yes. It might seem odd because ovulation – when you can get pregnant – occurs during the middle of your cycle, while your period is at the beginning of your cycle. But even though a pregnancy is unlikely, it can still happen. It depends on how long your cycle is and exactly when you ovulate (which isn't necessarily slap-bang in the middle of your cycle).

Once you ovulate, there is a 24–48-hour window when the egg can be fertilised. A pretty small window, right? Well, the thing is, sperm can live inside the womb for up to a week – so if you have sex a week before you ovulate, there's a chance you could still get pregnant. And if you have sex on day five of your cycle, when you're still on your period, and you ovulate on day 12, there's a chance you could get pregnant. Also, it's worth mentioning that because of this you can get pregnant before you've even had your first-ever period. If you have unprotected sex at the time just before or during your first ovulation, you could pregnant.

Great, glad we've cleared that up.

PART TWO

Contraception

Periods are the daily or monthly grind of where our hormone diaries begin, but it does not end there. If only we were so lucky!

Where do we even begin the shitshow and confusion that is contraception? It would be nice if there was a one-size-fits-all birth control, but unfortunately there isn't. It is a blessing and a curse how many different options there are. Great: you'll hopefully be able to find something that works for you. Not so great: where do you start with finding that out? It feels like an absolute minefield.

First off, none of the hormonal or non-hormonal contraception we're going to be talking about in this section can protect you from sexually tranmitted infections (STIs). Only condoms can do that as well as protect you from pregnancy. Condoms are just all-round great. They're non-hormonal, non-intrusive, easy, cheap (sometimes free!) and reliable. And I repeat: THE ONLY CONTRACEPTION THAT WILL PROTECT YOU FROM STIs.

Now on to the other methods. You'll find a comprehensive table of all the different types of contraception, how they work and their effectiveness in my first book *Doing It!*. But below is a list of your contraception options:

* **The pill**
(combined and progestogen-only)

* **Patch**

* **IUD**
(copper coil)

* **Implant**

* **Diaphragm**

* **Vaginal ring**

* **Injection**

* **Fertility awareness**

* **IUS**
(hormonal coil)

Most of the above require a visit to the doctor to get sorted out. Don't forget, in the UK you can go to your doctor or sexual-health clinic to get contraception, even if you're under 16 years old. The appointment is completely confidential. Many people under 16 go on contraception for a variety of reasons, so there is nothing to be worried or ashamed about.

Getting it right

You will often see percentage numbers given of the effectiveness of a certain type of contraception. It's important to know that this is referring to 'perfect use', which is not the same as 'typical use'. 'Perfect use' means you are taking the contraception 100 per cent as instructed, with no mistakes or hiccups. 'Typical use' is how us mere, flawed mortals, who will never be able to achieve perfection, use contraception. For example, used perfectly every time, condoms are 98 per cent effective at preventing pregnancy. However, sometimes it doesn't get put on properly or you forget to pinch the tip or you use Vaseline as lube (which is oil-based, a big no-no) and the next thing you know, condoms are 85 per cent effective with typical use. (There's a step-by-step guide on how to put on a condom in *Doing It!*, which you should read if you want to increase your chances of getting close to that 98 per cent effectiveness!)

For methods that rely on humans to take action, such as the pill, the patch and the vaginal ring, the difference between perfect and typical use can be significant. My favourite resource to demonstrate this is an interactive guide by *The New York Times*, which takes different birth control methods and plots them on a graph to show how many women out of one hundred will become pregnant from perfect and typical use over a ten-year period. The data is fascinating and what it shows is that the coil (copper and hormonal) and implant are by far the most effective methods – because you just get them put in once by a medical professional and there's practically no room for human error.

But people go on contraception for all sorts of reasons, not just to prevent pregnancy. As we've discussed, it's also used as a way of managing your period, any PMS symptoms or other conditions.

Dear my pill,

You, my friend, are a true friend. I started taking you when I was 15. Five years ago, that's 1,827 days. Well, probably closer to 1,800 (I'm sorry I forget about you sometimes).

Our friendship grew out of our combined dislike for my period. I had reached a stage where I could not take the pain any more – two days a month for three years were lost to standing up, sitting down, rolling around, crying, sleeping and being a right grump, followed by five days of whingeing that my uterus was mimicking the Niagara Falls.

And then you came along! *insert angel noises*
And you are great! You work alongside my
migraines, not putting me at any greater risk.
You're reliable, small and fit in my handbag.
Occasionally we fall out when you surprise
me with bloody knickers, but you tackled the
pain, length and quantity of my periods.
You rock!

You're here to comfort me, support me and stop
the demon inside being released. The fact that
you also protect me when I get laid is an
added bonus, but not your main job.

So, in fact …

Dear presumptions,

Me and my pill are pals! The galliest of all
pals. Our friendship has nothing to do with
sex, willies, sperm, pulling, sexuality, one-
night stands, my long-term partner or babies.
So when I casually throw into a conversation
something about my good ol' chum – please
don't presume. She and I go WAYYY back, and
our friendship is much stronger than a bit of
cuddling under the sheets.

Little pill pack, you keep doing you. Because
without you, I wouldn't be able to be me.

Matilda, UK

THE INFAMOUS PILL

When the pill was developed in the 1950s, it was a Big Deal. It was introduced in the UK in 1961 for married women only and then was made available for all women in 1967. My grandparents got married in 1962 and the family planning clinic refused to give her the pill – instead they gave her the diaphragm. My mum was born a year later. See where I'm going with this?

What is a diaphragm?

Rarely prescribed these days as it's not as reliable as other methods and is a bit of a faff, the diaphragm used to be a very common contraceptive. The diaphragm is a silicone dome that you insert into your vagina. It covers the cervix, preventing sperm from getting in the womb, but you also need to use spermicide with it which kills the sperm. You put it in before you have sex (you can put it in up to two hours before) and then you have to leave it in for at least six hours after you've finished. With perfect use it's 94 per cent effective, but with typical use it's only 88 per cent effective.

Nowadays the pill is one of the most, if not THE most, common of all contraceptives used. It'll be the first one your doctor tries you on unless you specifically ask for something else, or if they're a super-good doctor and talk you through all your options before prescribing it. I mean, that should be standard, but GP appointments rarely last long enough to have time to go through everything.

How the pill works

There are two types of the contraceptive pill. The most common is the combined pill; combined means there are two artificial hormones in it called oestrogen and progestogen. The other type of pill is the progestogen-only pill, sometimes called the 'mini-pill'. Other than the hormones they contain, the main difference between the two is that with the combined pill, you take it for 21 days and then, traditionally, have a seven-day break, or seven days of sugar pills, during which you'll have a withdrawal bleed. In contrast, the progestogen-only pill is taken continuously with no breaks.

Easy enough to understand, right? Well, turn the page to discover some new guidelines about the combined pill (and other combined hormonal contraception), which makes this slightly more complicated ...

BREAKING NEWS!

You may have noticed I slipped in the word 'traditionally' on the previous page. That's because there's recently been a big change in UK guidance around how we should use combined hormonal contraception (CHC), which includes the combined pill, the patch and the vaginal ring. In January 2019, new guidelines were released stating that there was no evidence that the seven-day hormone break had any health benefit and could, in fact, lead to a slightly increased risk of pregnancy (if people forget to start their next pill packet on the right day, for example). What?! On the one hand, I'm shocked that we're only just finding this out. But on the other, I'm glad that science is winning out and information is being updated as we learn more about contraception. But why did it take 60 years?!

Here's a quick overview of the alternative ways you could use CHC, which could reduce the risk of pregnancy.

Shortened break – 21 days on hormones, four days off.

Tricycling – 9 weeks (3 x 21 days) on, four or seven days off.

Flexible – use CHC continuously. If you see any breakthrough bleeding for three to four days, take a hormone-break for four days, then restart the CHC.

Continuous – no break from hormones.

The 21 days of hormones and then a seven-day break is still totally an option, and if that's what you feel most comfortable with, feel free to just carry on as you were. The next time (or the first time) you go to get your pill, patch or ring, talk to the doctor or nurse about the different options to figure out what will work best for you.

So how do oestrogen and progestogen work to prevent pregnancy? After all, aren't they the hormones involved in *preparing* your body for pregnancy? It does feel a bit strange that the hormones that help us get pregnant also prevent us from getting pregnant. So how does it work? This bit gets quite sciencey ...

Hormonal contraception contains synthetic versions of the natural hormones found in our body.

Synthetic oestrogen stops your body producing two other key hormones, follicle-stimulating hormone (FSH) and luteinising hormone (LH). FSH stimulates the growth of ovarian follicles, which contain eggs before they mature and get released during ovulation. An acute rise in LH is what actually triggers the ovulation. So with oestrogen preventing mature eggs becoming available and ovulation occurring, you can't get pregnant.

The second hormone is a bit more confusing because there is an ever-so-slight difference in name. The hormone found in the body is called progesterone. The synthetic hormone found in contraception is called progestogen. Progestogen thickens your cervical mucus, making it difficult for sperm to get through, and also thins the lining of the uterus, making it more difficult for a fertilised egg to implant successfully. Some progestogen-only pills contain a progestogen called desogestrel, which also prevents ovulation.

How to remember to take the pill

One of the downsides to the pill is that you have to remember to take it every day – so it has huge amounts of room for human error. If you are ever late taking your pill or completely forget it or you vomit soon after taking it, then do be aware that you're not fully covered. Check with your doctor or read the packaging of your specific pill for what to do if you miss one, and use alternative contraceptive methods for a week.

The below is a general guide to help you remember to take your pill, but check the specifics of the one you're on – some require

you to take it at *exactly* the same time every day, others have a window of a few hours, others have one as long as 12 hours.

Set an alarm on your phone.

Tell your housemates, partner or family (whoever lives with you) your pill-taking schedule so they can hold you accountable and remind you.

Keep it on your bedside table or in your bag.

If there's another person's house that you stay over at a lot, maybe leave a pill packet there.

Combine it with an existing daily routine or habit such as brushing your teeth.

Track the days you take your pill in a period-tracking app.

The day you open your last packet, make an appointment to get some more (that gives you four weeks' notice so you don't run out!). You can even set calendar reminders of when to book new appointments.

If you know you're going away, make sure you have enough pills beforehand. Also check the specifics of your pill about what to do if you're travelling in different time zones.

If you're reading this thinking, 'But I am a mere human prone to forgetfulness and the occasional vomit – help me!', don't panic. There are plenty of other contraceptive methods out there, and these are covered in the next chapter.

What's the right pill for you?

Dear my pill,

I can't thank you enough for the splendid years we had together. It was a bit difficult at first because I was new to this contraception game and most of my friends were on the combined pill if anything. None of us really knew what we were doing, but because you worked slightly differently to the other pills, I couldn't ask my friends for help. I never had to set a reminder alarm on my phone because you had a 12-hour window I could take you in and I'd still be covered. I couldn't quite believe it, so every so often I would re-read your instructions to make sure I'd got that right. It was very handy for long-distance travel and changing time zones.

The other difference was that I never took a break from you. Not even a week of placebo, it was hormones every day baby! (Except no babies.) You became part of my daily routine.

Thanks for the memories, thanks for protecting my boobs and uterus from pain and thanks for getting rid of my period for seven years.

Much appreciated,

Hannah
x

I was 17 when I first went on the pill. I'd heard about implants, injections and the coil, but didn't really understand them and they seemed scary, so I went to my doctor asking to be put on the pill. They asked for my medical history and so I told them about having ulcerative colitis. Instead of the combined pill that most of my friends were on, I was put on the progestogen-only pill. This is because of potential effects of the combined pill on bone density, and as someone with a form of inflammatory bowel disease (IBD), I was already at a higher risk of low bone density and osteoporosis. I had no idea that bone density was linked to IBD or contraception until my doctor said something about bones and gave me a different pill.

So, when you're going for that first appointment to get contraception, tell your doctor *everything* about your medical history. Even if you don't think it's relevant, it might be and they'll be the person to know. Or they can at least refer you to someone who does. Ultimately, doctors are there to help us. And with all the knowledge they have, they will try to make the best decision for us. That doesn't mean you can't get a second opinion – absolutely do that! For example, bone density is a bit of a controversial area in medicine – some doctors think that oral contraceptive pills *protect* bone density rather than damage it. Science often isn't as black and white as we might want it to be.

I got extremely lucky aged 17 – the first pill I was prescribed worked wonders for me. I didn't get pregnant (that's the bare minimum you ask of your contraceptive, right?), I didn't notice any negative side effects and my periods stopped (which at the time I was very grateful for). It was a breeze. But I know there'll be a lot of you reading this right now thinking how unfair that is.

Every pill affects every person differently. Even if you find someone who has exactly the same kind of period and PMS symptoms, and is the same age, height and weight as you and has a pill that works for them – guess what, it won't necessarily work the same for you. There are no cheats or gaming the system to be had here, it's a puzzle that changes every time you attempt to complete it.

Dear current brand of birth control pills,

I appreciate you helping to regulate my period, controlling my pimples (for the most part) and keeping me from getting pregnant. But could you please keep periods to the minimum? The last few months have not been fun – where I get a random breakthrough period for NO REASON that lasts ALMOST AS LONG AS MY NORMAL PERIOD! And then I do get my normal period still.

Please STOP! I've talked to my doctor and if you continue to do this, we might need to break up. Just do your job!

Thanks!
Brigit, USA

Going on or coming off the pill can affect your mood and your body. The various possible side effects are like a pick 'n' mix, but you don't get to decide what goes in your bag and it's all a bit of a surprise. There are definitely some patterns though.

Doctors might prescribe you a specific pill because it's known to reduce acne or mood swings or may lighten your period. So if you experience really heavy or painful periods or you're struggling with some PMS symptoms, the pill or other hormone contraception might be able to help. I say 'might' because, as we know, there really is no one-size-fits-all. Fingers crossed that whatever you choose works for you, eh!

Dear pill,

We've been through a lot together. I don't really remember my (period) life without you. We've been having periods together longer than we have apart. But I think it is time for us to spend some time apart. Don't get me wrong, we have had some great times together, and you stopped me having major inconveniences when I didn't need them, which I will for ever be thankful for. Remember the day my mam found out about you and shit hit the fan? That was not fun.

It's not you, it's me. I just don't know if you've changed me as a person or if you are the reason I have gained weight, or if it is just to do with all the growing up I've been doing over the past five years. This was not an easy decision to make but it is the right time, especially

That doesn't sound fun. But remember, in the UK you are allowed to be prescribed contraception without parental consent.

as we don't have a third party to worry about any more.

I'm sure there are thousands of girls out there that you will make equally as happy. You will always have a special place on my bedside table.

Josephine, UK

Other side effects

Weight Gain

One thing that has always cropped up around the internet, among friends and in magazines is a worry that the pill causes weight gain. And yes, there is a possibility that it will, but don't let that stop you trying it.

In my case, it was actually when I was coming off the pill aged 24 that I noticed weight change – I gained rather than lost it. It took me a while to clock that I was no longer fitting into my bras and clothes. I don't know about you, but when my weight changes, the first place it goes to or drops off is my boobs, and bras are damn expensive. I can't afford to keep buying new ones every time my weight changes! As nothing had really changed in my life during that time apart from coming off the pill, it was very likely the hormone change in a system that had been the same for seven years. Whether you gain weight on or off the pill, weight changes are a reality for many in relation to its use.

Depression and mood changes

Dear mini-pill,

I will never quite forgive you for making me feel so low that I spent hours on the bathroom floor, sobbing my heart out and wanting to self-harm. I will also never forgive the doctor that prescribed you even when I told her that the combined pill worked for me. But at the same time, you brought me so low that I finally sought the help I needed by getting therapy and making my overall mental health much better. I resent it, but thank you regardless.

Not a lot of love from,
Nikki, UK

In 2016, a groundbreaking Danish study was published in the *Journal of the American Medical Association Psychiatry* that found a connection between taking the pill and depression. It wasn't groundbreaking in the sense of it being surprising, since people on the pill have been thinking this for years, but only now are their experiences actually backed up by data. It means that patients will hopefully be taken seriously now when they go to the doctor saying they've been feeling low since going on the pill. There are alternatives and you don't have to suffer because of your contraception.

Dear pill,

I've tried so many different versions of you, but I just can't have you in my life. You made me so depressed during PMS that I almost dropped out of uni. Twice you made me throw up so much that my mum thought I had morning sickness. You made me paranoid, thinking my boyfriend was cheating on me, and you killed my libido so much it was pointless taking you. So thanks for stopping me from getting pregnant for years and giving me the regular periods I never had, but I need to put my mental health first.

Niamh, UK

It's not just depression that can be a side effect of the pill – there can be other mood changes too. One of my friends was on a pill that caused her natural ups and downs to go to the extreme so she felt manic and unstable; thankfully, it settled when she switched to a different pill. If you're trying new contraception, keeping track of your mood is absolutely a thing you can be doing if you want to figure out if there's a pattern in your mood swings, or just want to keep a record. And I'll say it again: you don't have to suffer for your contraception.

Dear combined pill,

Thank you for stabilising my crazy PMS mood swings so that I could get my mental illness diagnosis and treatment. My brain was a ticking time bomb that was masked by hormonal highs and lows, and now I have control of my health.

Sincerely,
Rebecca, UK

I've heard countless stories about how the pill has affected people's moods and I'm still no closer to understanding how or why. The lack of research combined with the stigma around mental health feels like we're in the dark even more than normal on this one. That crossover can lead to a lot of people suffering alone with no idea why as they're told it's a 'normal part of being a woman'. There are many parts of a woman's life that we grow up being told will hurt or should hurt – that it's 'normal' to hurt from: period pains, sex, mood swings, childbirth. Okay, that last one does come with a fair expectation of pain, but all the others don't have to. There are ways to reduce pain or avoid it. You should never feel like you have to settle for pain, physical or mental, because you've been told it's natural or normal. *You don't have to feel pain.*

The dark history of the pill

The pill is often seen as a symbol of women's liberation. When it was developed, it was the first time that people with wombs could truly take their reproductive futures into their own hands (or mouths), and their lives and choices were no longer dictated by their biology. However, there is a dark side to the pill and its history.

The contraceptive pill was developed by American scientists led by Dr Gregory Pincus with the help of birth control advocate Margaret Sanger. Unusually for the time, it was also funded by a woman, suffragist Katherine McCormick. In the first clinical trials of the pill, women weren't told what its intended effect was (which was common practice in medical tests in the 1950s). Many subjects dropped out of the trials due to side effects such as dizziness, nausea, bloating, blood clots and mood changes (sound familiar?). In trials in Puerto Rico, there were lots of complaints of side effects, and three women even died during the study at the Rio Piedras clinic, but no autopsies were done so we don't know if this was caused by the pill. Either way, it was approved by the Food and Drug Administration (FDA) in the USA in 1960 because it worked for its intended purpose (preventing pregnancy) despite the side effects.

Britain undertook its own clinical trials (with varying results) and birth control pills became available on the NHS in December 1961. Previously, contraception had been the responsibility of charity groups and family planning clinics, but with the birth of the pill, the medical profession became more involved. However, it wasn't until 1967 that doctors could give birth control advice to unmarried women and all contraceptive advice and supplies became free of charge on the NHS regardless of age or marital status in 1974. This is what allows under-16s to go to the GP to get the pill without their parents' knowledge or consent. Getting there wasn't easy though; a mother named Victoria Gillick campaigned to prevent her teenage daughters being given contraceptive advice by NHS doctors, but ultimately her attempts were futile.

We now know that the level of hormones in the first pill was much higher than was necessary to prevent pregnancy (10,000 micrograms of progestogen and 150 micrograms of oestrogen, compared to 50–150 and 20–50 now respectively). This contributed to the increased likelihood and severity of the side effects seen in the clinical trials. In the USA, it wasn't until damning Senate investigations called the 'Nelson hearings' were held in 1970 that the hormone dosage was reduced and potential side effects had to be listed on an insert in each pill packet. Hundreds of women wrote letters to the FDA during these hearings, demanding they be given information about the side effects of the pill and feminists demonstrated because not one woman was invited to speak at the hearings. Just one of many examples in politics of decisions being made about women's bodies with no women present. Even when an insert listing potential side effects was produced, the American Medical Association (AMA) opposed it and the FDA supported this opposition – though they did recommend that doctors give the information to women prescribed the pill. This didn't become enforceable until 1980, however, and even now it feels like the battle for information about our bodies and what we put in them continues.

This puts the recent revelation about the Catholic Church and the withdrawal bleed in context. The pill was originally pitched to include a break from the medication, leading to a withdrawal bleed, to appease anti-contraceptioners and seem more 'natural'. This 'need' for a fake period seems astonishing – not only because it signals that religious interference was rife in the 1960s, but also because it's only coming to light now. However, the story is more complicated. There were many reasons why a break in the pill was introduced – and appeasing the Catholic Church was only one of them. As we now know, the original pill had significantly more hormones in it than the one we know today, which made the side effects more regular and severe. The seven-day break was also introduced to give pill-takers a well-deserved break from the sheer amount of hormones entering their bodies. Also, this kind of contraception wasn't just new and scary to the Catholic Church – it was new to everyone! There was a lot of anxiety about how it affected the body and having regular bleeding was seen as reassurance that *phew, I'm not pregnant*! (Although that is totally incorrect – a withdrawal bleed whilst on combined contraception is no guarantee that you are not pregnant.) So as much as it can be satisfying to blame the Catholic Church for all the bad things that have happened to women, in this case it's only partly to blame.

There's a lot of debate amongst historians about whether or not the pill was truly liberating. Yes, it meant women could separate sex from reproduction – but with that realisation, a truly terrifying train of thought emerged from some of the menfolk: 'If the risk of getting pregnant has been taken off the table, what legitimate reason could a woman possibly have for

refusing sex?'
So did the pill make it
harder for women to
say 'no' to sex? And
did men assume a
woman on the pill
would always be
'up for it'?

Obviously, there are many reasons why someone might not want to have sex with someone, and they are ALL valid. If someone doesn't want to have sex with you, or is unsure if they want to have sex with you, don't have sex with them.

There's also the assumption that once someone is on the pill there's no further need to manage sexual health. How many times have you heard, 'We didn't use a condom because she was on the pill'? Too many to count. This stuff isn't necessarily the pill's fault though – it's society's. The culture we live in is non-consensual, sexist and full of double standards. But we're changing that, right? We have to.

THE HORMONAL CONTRACEPTION YOU WEREN'T TAUGHT ABOUT IN SCHOOL

It's important to know that there are other options out there other than the pill. Different methods to suit different people's needs and lifestyles. Here are some other hormonal contraceptives that don't get as much attention as the pill.

The injection

A hormone injection contains progestogen and is injected into your muscle, usually your bum or upper arm, by a doctor or health professional (don't worry, not you or your friend!). Depending on which type you get, it can last from 8 to 13 weeks. The upside: as soon as it's injected, you don't have to think about contraception again until it's time for the next jab, woohoo! The downsides: you have to remember to book that next injection appointment, and if you experience any nasty side effects, you can't just stop taking it – you have to wait until your full 8–13 weeks is up and the hormones have left the body.

Dear injection,

It's not you, it's me. It's been a great run, but we both knew that it couldn't last forever.

This doesn't mean that I don't love you – we had so many good years together. Sure I got stabbed in the buns every three months, but for a life free of crippling periods, lovely skin AND no babies, you were the best. And you introduced me to who I think will be a lifelong friend, progesterone. I'm moving on with the coil, but I'll never forget you. I hope you meet lots of other people and make them as happy as you've made me.

Love,
Rachel, UK

The patch

The patch is a small patch (duh) that sticks to your skin like a plaster and is usually worn on the upper arm. It contains oestrogen and progestogen, which it releases into your body to prevent pregnancy. One patch lasts one week, then you take it off and swap it for another patch. You do this for at least three weeks. As the patch is a combined hormonal contraceptive, there are different ways to use it: with a seven-day hormonal break and withdrawal bleed, or one of the alternative options I outlined earlier. You can wear the patch in the bath, swimming and doing sports, but it is visible on the skin.

Dear patch,

Thank you for regulating my periods and helping me ease my period pains. I wish you could've done it without making me gain a lot of weight, although I think it has made me have a better relationship with my body … it's bittersweet. You've made me so much more safe with my body, my relationships, and my sex life.

Greta, Sweden

Vaginal ring

The vaginal ring is a small, soft plastic ring that you insert into your vagina yourself, which contains oestrogen and progestogen. With clean hands, you pinch it and insert it with your fingers and gently push it up until it feels comfortable. It can't get lost inside you and you can still have sex, use tampons and menstrual cups. You leave it in for 21 days and then take it out by inserting your finger, hooking it around and pulling it out. Don't flush it down the toilet! It should come with a disposable bag to throw it away in. You can then put a new one in for another 21 days or have a withdrawal bleed – it's another one of those combined hormonal contraceptives.

IT'S NO LARCING MATTER

LARC does exactly what it says on the tin. It's a long-lasting and reversible form of contraception. LARC methods include the implant and the coil (both hormonal and copper). It's reversible because, unlike the pill and the injection – which, once they're in, they're in – all you need is a medical professional to remove it and it stops working. The hormonal coil also releases lower levels of hormones because it's already in the uterus so they don't have far to travel.

The implant

The implant, also known as the rod, is a small bar that gets inserted into your upper arm and releases the hormone progestogen into your bloodstream. It must be inserted or taken out by a doctor or nurse, and lasts for three years. I've been told by friends that getting it inserted isn't painful, but once it's in you can kind of see and feel it under your skin which can be weird. You can get it taken out at any time within the three years, and when you get it removed, it can be replaced by another one.

The implant is great for people who just want to have reliable contraception for a few years and not have to worry about it.

However, as with all contraception, there are side effects and it's unpredictable if or to what extent they will affect you.

Dear implant,

You little attractive darling — how ideal you are in theory! Years of protection with very little effort needed on my part is such a wonder. And might I also say, thank you, oh thank you, for the return of my sexual urges after coming off the pill!

But oh little wonder, how you have made me bleed. Three straight months of minor yet constant bleeding and/or discharge. Tampons are not my style, so you necessitated three straight months of pads and liners, which in turn brought yeast infection and intense irritation. Dear implant, please let my body breathe.

Yours for three more years,
Madrona, USA

The coil

The coil is a small T-shaped device that is inserted into your womb. Depending on which one you get, it lasts between five and 10 years. There are two types, known in the UK as the IUD (intrauterine device), which is non-hormonal and made out of copper, and the IUS (intrauterine system) which has a low dosage of hormones.

A little theory of mine

In the animated film *Megamind*, released in 2010, the villain (Megamind) finally defeats the hero he's spent his whole life fighting against. The hero is your stereotypical macho male and embodies the idealised superhero masculinity. He is 'defeated' (spoilers) because Megamind traps him in a room made of copper and copper weakens his powers so he can't escape. Why is this relevant, Hannah, I hear you ask? Well, how do you think the IUD works without any hormones in it? COPPER IS TOXIC TO SPERM!

I would just really love to know if the writers of *Megamind* knew this and that's why they chose copper to kill off the hyper-masculine character. Surely it can't be a coincidence.

The IUD has been known to make periods heavier or longer, but conversely, the IUS can make your periods lighter, shorter or even stop altogether. However, the IUS can also come with other side effects such as mood swings, skin problems or sore boobs.

Since Halloween 2017, I've had the IUS. It has a low dosage of progestogen, which is the same hormone that was in the pill I'd been taking for years beforehand. It lasts for five years so, unless I decide to remove it sooner, I'll have it until Halloween 2022. By then, I will be 30 years old – prime baby-making age by our society's standards. Decision time: second coil or first baby? Obviously I'm not deciding now, but it does make me think. The year 2022 is also when I'm due to get a new passport – it's clearly going to be a big year.

Dear IUD,

I love you. You've changed my life for the better in so many ways. With years of struggling with oral contraceptives and the implant and experiencing absolutely awful side effects from the hormones, I'm so grateful to have finally found you.

It's upsetting that we aren't taught about you in school, or in the media, or even when I was in the hospital telling them that I thought the hormones in the rod may have had something to do with my depression. It's such a safe, cost-effective, easily reversible form of contraception, without all the nasty side effects!

Here in Australia, you're offered for free to people who are needing or wanting to get an abortion as an easy way to prevent people from ending up in the same situation in the future.

You're the bomb, IUD!

Lots of love,
Emily, Australia

In the UK, the copper IUD is also offered as an emergency contraceptive. It is 99 per cent effective at preventing pregnancy after unprotected sex and can be inserted (by a professional) up to five days after, so it is more effective than the emergency contraceptive pill. Also, you can then continue using it as a regular contraceptive for up to ten years.

Getting the coil
My story of getting the IUS a.k.a hormonal coil.

Beforehand
Everyone tells you how painful getting the coil is and I was terrified going into my appointment, and I'm not going to lie, it isn't comfortable – it involves a doctor pushing something through your cervix to get to your uterus.

There are different types of coil and different brands of the IUS in the UK, with differing hormone levels and sizes, so ask about these. Go through the different options with the clinic before your coil is fitted. Ask questions, especially when it comes to how the coil will affect your periods. The copper IUD, for example, has been known to make periods heavier and more painful, which may be outweighed by its other benefits for you, but be informed so YOU can make the decision about what you get.

Good lord, I have no idea how the cervix opens wide enough to fit a baby through it. How? How?! When I was younger I used to think that the whole '10-cm dilated' thing was referring to your vagina – how wrong I was. I don't think I even knew the cervix existed then (this is why sex ed is important, folks!). Thankfully, I went into my coil appointment fully aware of where my cervix is.

I would like to flag up at this point that making a LARC appointment is often not straightforward. If, as in my case, your GP doesn't have someone that does LARC insertions, you will have to go to a specialist contraception and sexual-health clinic.

And (like mine) your regular GP might not refer you, and you'll have to look online, find a clinic, contact them and self-refer. This can be a long and infuriating process; I called a whole bunch of different numbers only to find out I was trying to reach a clinic that had closed down! Finally, I got through to somewhere but then had to book the appointment online, without any sort of consultation first. What I'm saying is, be prepared to do research and be patient if you've decided the coil may be your best contraceptive option.

The insertion

There was a doctor and a nurse at my appointment. I lay on the table/bed thing with my jeans and underwear off and knees bent (no legs in stirrups). They asked if I would like a numbing injection and I said yes, even though I had taken some paracetamol before my appointment as advised. I didn't even realise this was a thing they could offer! The injection did hurt, like a really sharp scratch on my cervix, probably a little more painful than my smear test, but the good news is that the numbing clearly worked because I felt nothing after that. I had no idea when the doctor put the coil in and I had to ask 'Is it done?' They didn't rush me, and they let me take my time sitting up and getting dressed. Then I sat in the waiting room for 15 minutes so they could make sure I was okay before sending me home.

After the procedure it is common for your body to want to reject the foreign object inside it. This is normal and I had been warned about it, but it can be scary if you aren't aware that it is a natural response. I began to get strong cramps on my way to the tube from the clinic and felt faint and a bit sick. My advice is grab some painkillers, go home, put your PJs on, fill a hot water bottle and climb into bed – like I did. When I woke up hours later, I felt so much better. I was still in a little bit of pain, but it was more like the cramps I get on day one of my period and I didn't feel sick any more. So I spent Halloween 2017 in bed by myself watching Netflix. I didn't even watch scary films.

The aftermath

For about a month afterwards, I just spotted: every day there was a small amount of blood in my pants. Some days I wore panty liners, some days I wore period underwear and other days I just wore normal black underwear because I could not be arsed – free-bleeding a few drops of blood seemed fine. But after that, things got a bit more eyebrow-raising.

The coil I had inserted had the same hormones in as the pill I was on previously, though with a much lower dosage, so I felt like I knew what I was getting myself into. But two months later, I was in hospital with the worst flare-up of my UC I'd ever had. I was in hospital for four weeks and needed emergency surgery to remove my colon – I now live with a stoma bag.

I don't know if getting the coil and my flare-up are connected. My head says no, it was just a coincidence. But my gut (pun intended) says, maybe? UC is an auto-immune disease where my immune system thinks my bowel is a dangerous foreign body and attacks itself. It's also really unpredictable. Everyone with UC is affected differently and doctors are still trying to figure out what can potentially cause it or trigger flare-ups. When I asked if there was any connection, I was always met with the same response: 'There's no evidence that hormonal contraception and UC are connected.' But that's the same answer that many people experiencing depression after going on the pill received: that there was no connection between depression and contraception. It was only in 2016 that the first study actually linked the two. I guess I'm just holding out hope for more and more research so we can all make better and more informed decisions about our health.

I don't want to scare you – my case is an extreme one. It's very normal to have debilitating cramps after you get the coil inserted. They're caused by your body sensing a foreign object inside you and thinking 'Bad!', then trying to attack it and push it out. Still, it's worth being aware of what your body is telling you. I've always been pretty good at telling the difference between my period cramps and my IBD cramps – they feel different and come from different parts of the body. But because I'd just got the coil inserted, I was in new territory. After the initial horrendous post-insertion pain, I would get these little piercing cramps every so often that gradually increased in regularity and pain. Now I know that this was the early sign of my UC flare-up, but at the time I thought it was just my body adjusting to the coil. If you notice anything out of the ordinary about your body after getting the coil, I encourage you to go to your doctors.

After about a month of spotting into panty liners, my bleeding stopped completely when my ulcerative colitis symptoms really started to pick up. Thankfully, throughout my entire flare-up and time in hospital, I didn't have any periods or spotting. My chronic illness had overridden any other normal bodily behaviours like my menstrual cycle. Sure enough, once I was on the road to recovery and I was out of hospital, eating normally again and gaining back the weight I'd lost, I had a period! My boobs started aching on 22 March 2018 and then my period came on 28 March. How do I know that? Because I used a period-tracking app and that's what it tells me!

I was so grateful. After everything I'd been through, getting my period was a sign that my body was functioning normally and healthily again. But that was my last proper period. My body let me have that last period as a final hurrah and then the coil took over. I had a sort of mini period in May – I can't really remember what this was like, but my app says I had sore boobs and then light bleeding and cramps. And I've had nothing since. Not even sore boobs! Hurray!

2019 update: sporadic sore boobs have returned. Why, oh why?!

Dear coil,

We've been roommates in this body for over a year now and I realized I've never properly introduced myself. How rude! My name is Hannah, I'm turning 21 in a week and I really don't want a baby for my birthday. You made a lot of lofty promises when you first came into my life about how you would shorten or even get rid of my period completely, give me *fewer cramps, and most importantly make sure a third party didn't set up camp in there. While you've done a good job warding off unwanted guests, my period got longer and my cramps might have improved a microscopic bit but it also might just be my imagination. I do have to say though you're doing your main job remarkably well and for that I am eternally grateful.*

I hope we can remain friends for the two years we have left until I replace you. Sorry in advance for that, we just weren't meant to be together forever.

Love,
Hannah, Switzerland

Coil aftercare

The bottom of the coil has two strings that hang down through the cervix and into the vagina. It's recommended you check to feel these every month. If you can't feel the strings, there's a possibility that the coil has moved and may no longer be effective. In this case, make an appointment with your GP or at your nearest sexual-health clinic. I also recently read on the NHS website that you're supposed to have a follow-up appointment three to six weeks after getting the coil inserted to make sure everything is fine. This wasn't offered to me and I didn't realise this was a thing at the time, so I would recommend asking about it.

Dear my first coil,

You were so good to me. We met when I was 17 and I really had no idea what I was inviting into my body for five years. But you were a good roommate in this body of mine. You were with me through so many exciting and new things: leaving school, moving to a new city, university, the sex stuff. You took my period away, but had the decency to provide a monthly ovulation-cramp to let me know you were doing your job. It feels kind of weird that I've moved three times in those five years and always took the same, unopened box of emergency-tampons with me.

But last year you moved out. You were replaced. Funnily enough, it was also the first time I also took a proper look at you. As I was sitting in the gynaecological chair, local anaesthesia and painkillers working their magic, the nurse asked me if I wanted to keep you and I just loudly said 'YES PLEASE'. Five minutes later, the nurse handed you to me. You were simultaneously bigger and smaller than I expected. And I got strangely emotional. You had been with me for five whole years. Every step of the way, just doing your thing while I was doing mine.

You are still in my room, tucked away so nobody stumbles upon you by mistake.

This is weird and wonderful. I had no idea you could potentially keep your old coils and I'm definitely going to ask to keep mine!

I don't think I will ever throw you away.
Sometimes I just like to remember how amazing
science and bodies are by looking at you.

In Liebe,
Hannah, Germany

O LIBIDO, LIBIDO, WHEREFORE ART THOU LIBIDO?

It's been mentioned a couple of times already, but I would like to make the space to address libido here. I remember when I first started documenting my journey with *The Hormone Diaries*, a change in libido was something I was interested in learning about. Is there a pattern? Does hormonal contraception really affect your sexual urges? Overwhelmingly, when I tried to find scientific research to answer these questions, all I found out was 'Maybe, who knows'. No surprises there.

Of course, you might not be feeling any sexual urges yet, or you may not feel sexual attraction, and that's completely fine. And while some people experience a natural change in their libido during their cycle, others don't. I was always the latter. I never noticed any pattern of noticeable changes in my sexual urges (nor when I came off the pill). But you might find that you're super-horny around ovulation (oh, classic Mother Nature screaming at us to have babies) and also perhaps a little hornier than usual when on your period. Remember, there's nothing wrong with having sex on your period (see page 73) and it's completely healthy! Or it might be the case that you feel super-unsexy and your libido is low during your period; maybe you have heavy and painful periods or your PMS symptoms might really ruin the mood. Normal but potentially annoying. Many things can affect your libido.

Dear pill,

Thank you for taking away my periods and thus some of the pain my endometriosis afflicts on my body. However, could you possibly give me my libido back? The boyfriend and I would greatly appreciate it!

Cheers,
Joséphine, France

In theory, contraception can affect your libido because it's fiddling with your sex hormones. But the reality is that some people report a decreased libido, others report an increased libido and the majority report no change. And as with most other contraceptive side effects, it's impossible to predict. If your libido is affected, I imagine it is very frustrating. *Here's a pill so you can have sex without worrying about pregnancy. PSYCH! We've taken away your sex drive!*

If you think it's a hormonal change that has increased or decreased your libido and you don't like it, you can always change your contraception. There is nothing wrong with your sex life being important to you and wanting to be horny.

Dear libido,

Where the heck did you go? We were having such a great time and then you just disappeared. My boyfriend and I haven't had sex in months and I can tell it affects him, but I am just never in the mood. Just last year we were having sex several times a day, and now I'm lucky if I want to do it every month.

Seriously, what changed? I've been on the same pill for years and have had no negative side effects, so it can't be that. I'm definitely still attracted to my boyfriend, so it can't be that. I just can't pinpoint anything that might have made you want to leave. And it's not that I don't want to have sex, I really do, but whenever it comes down to the moment, I just can't get aroused or excited enough to go through with it. Please, please, come back, I really miss you.

Love,
Naomi, UK

Getting in the mood

One of the best ways I've had arousal explained to me was in Dr Emily Nagoski's book *Come As You Are* (great title). She likens your sexual excitement to being like a car accelerator and your sexual inhibitor to being like the brakes. Everyone is different in terms of the sensitivity of their accelerator and brakes, and everyone has got different things that might trigger either one of them – your turn-ons and turn-offs. Your accelerator responds to any 'sexually relevant' stimulation and your brakes respond to any 'potential threats' – anything you see, hear, touch, taste, smell or imagine. So here's your very simple guide to getting horny:

Figure out your turn-ons and turn-offs.

Turn on the ons, turn off the offs.

Got it? Thanks Emily!

Dear gynaecologist,

I wish you had warned me that lack of libido was a potential side effect of the pill, even if it's not common. And I wish you hadn't been dismissive when I told you what I was feeling. My feelings were valid. I know it doesn't happen to many women but it DID happen to me. I was an 18-year-old scared to admit that I thought I was broken. It took a hell of a lot of courage to tell you I had absolutely no libido. And you had the nerve to shut me down, to question how I could know I had no libido if I was a virgin. Newsflash: many women masturbate, and even if I didn't, I still knew what it meant to be turned on. And when I informed you of this, you felt it was appropriate to say that if I wasn't having sex it didn't matter.

You didn't do your job and address the medication, you acted as if I was the problem. You made me think there was something wrong with me as a woman. It made me question my sexuality. I thought maybe I wasn't interested in dating men because I didn't realise I was gay. Or maybe I was asexual and had no idea. I went through an incredibly stressful year of questioning who I was only to realize that the pill was the problem, despite what you said. It's been six months since I've gotten off the pill and I'm still dealing with the repercussions of questioning my identity for

*so long. I'm still mad at you for making me
think I didn't know who I was. Who knew that a
tiny little pill and a ten-minute conversation
with a doctor could have that much power?*

Melanie, USA

There are so many different side effects to hormonal
contraception, some more mysterious than others, some more
common than others. Changes to our bodies, changes to our
mind and behaviour. Sometimes contraception helps to alleviate
PMS symptoms and other times it just creates more problems.
So it's no surprise that non-hormonal contraceptive methods
hold a certain allure. First of all, I'll say it again: CONDOMS ARE
NON-HORMONAL CONTRACEPTION. But if you want to hear
about another non-hormonal approach, read on.

DOES FERTILITY AWARENESS WORK?

The fertility awareness method works by tracking your cycle via various methods in order to determine your fertile window. This method is more commonly used by people who are actively trying to get pregnant, but in theory it works the same if you're trying to prevent pregnancy. You just avoid sex during your fertile window instead of actively trying to bang as much as possible during that time. Once you know your fertile window, you can avoid sex or use other contraceptive methods, such as condoms.

Time to address the elephant in the room. Fertility awareness has got a lot more press recently due to fertility apps becoming available and a general cultural shift towards a 'more natural' existence – but it's also made headlines when results have turned out to be less than great. I tried one of the apps for a while before quickly realising that it wasn't for me. And I can't stress that enough: fertility awareness is NOT for everyone. It has a very high pregnancy rate with 'typical use' – and the need for absolute perfection to successfully use this method is one reason why it generally isn't talked about in schools. The effectiveness of this method depends on your cycle and your lifestyle so if it's not going to work for you, it's not going to work. Don't try to force it, just accept it and move on.

How does fertility awareness work?

To track your fertility, the three things you measure and monitor are:

1. **The length of your cycle.**

2. **Your daily basal body temperature.**

Basal means your lowest body temperature at rest, usually during sleep. So you have to measure your temperature first thing in the morning before you get out of bed.

3. **Changes to your cervical mucus.**

As discussed, you can track your cycle's length using an app. To monitor your temperature, there is a specially designed app available, or you can buy yourself a special thermometer and monitor and record it yourself on a chart.

Temperature

You need a digital thermometer or one specifically designed for natural family planning. Take your temperature first thing in the morning before you get up and before you eat or drink anything, ideally at the same time every day. Plot your temperature on a graph. Your temperature will rise slightly after ovulation (about 0.2°C).

Cervical mucus

Put your finger gently inside your vagina. For the first few days after menstruation, the vagina usually feels dry and there is no mucus. In the lead-up to ovulation, the mucus may start to be moist, sticky, white and creamy. Immediately before ovulation it will get wetter, clearer and more slippery. It will then go back to being thicker and sticky.

Use condoms for at least the first three months when you start measuring – it takes time before you can start accurately finding your fertile window. If you've just come off hormonal contraception, you particularly need to give your body time to adjust.

There are specialist health professionals who can teach you how to measure your temperature, how to check your cervical mucus, record your findings and interpret the data. If this is a method you are seriously considering, do as much research as possible and get a professional to teach you. There is a lot of room for human error with fertility awareness. So if you struggle to remember to take the pill every day, I would not recommend this method – all the measuring takes commitment and practice.

Who does this method work for?

There are many factors that can affect the accuracy and effectiveness of fertility awareness, and it's important to be aware of them all. Sickness, hangovers, mixed sleeping patterns and travel can all affect your basal temperature readings. Remember, there are many things that can affect your menstrual cycle too, such as stress, weight change and illness.

This is the criteria that the ideal user of fertility awareness would fulfil. If you don't fit the bill, then I'd advise you not to bother.

In a relationship

Regular and predictable menstrual cycle

Regular sleep routine

Doesn't travel across time zones a lot

Healthy (doesn't get many colds, fevers)

Doesn't drink a lot

Getting pregnant wouldn't be the end of the world for you.

Think about it. How awful would it be if you accidentally got pregnant? If the answer is really awful, then pick a different method.

If this method is used properly by the right person then it can be very effective, and it can be really empowering for some people since it forces you to be in tune with your body and know exactly what is going on during your cycle. Personally, I am definitely *not* the right person for fertility awareness. My menstrual cycle is completely erratic, the amount of sleep I get varies on the weekends, I have the odd hangover, I travel and I have a chronic illness. But do your research and some serious thinking, and decide if it might work for you.

Dear fertility awareness app,

Artificial hormones were never my friend; I have tried three different pills, all of which have messed with either my mental health or my character. I found out about you through a YouTuber who works with you and got very excited when my thermometer arrived (along with loads of free condoms! Yay!).

I told the app everything it needed to know and said goodbye to the pill for good. I was 18 at the time and in a committed relationship. I took my measuring and general cycle awareness very seriously. My cycle was very regular and easy to follow after a while. My partner and I used condoms even on the most safe days just to be sure and were extra-cautious on the risky ones, we really didn't leave anything to chance. The longer my cycle stayed stable, the more we could relax and enjoy sex.

At a check-up after about seven months, my gynaecologist happened to mention he could see I had just ovulated. I remember thinking back in my head: three days before that we had skipped the condom because my ovulation wasn't due for another 15 days. I still don't know why my body decided to cut the month short. I wasn't stressed nor had I changed anything in my lifestyle or routine. My rising temperature should have been the indication that I was ovulating earlier than usual, but you just passed it off as an irregularity.

The following month my partner and I just hoped that by some miracle I wouldn't get pregnant – but I did. We both knew we weren't going to be parents at that point in our lives, if ever. The decision we made was accepted easily by my doctors and I feel very grateful to have had that freedom.

The day I found out was about four months ago. My new gynaecologist found a pill for me that is very suited to my needs. Today I cannot be anything but grateful for what happened, for letting me grow in a way I otherwise couldn't have. So thank you, little app, for trying to make me believe my body is a machine I can measure and count on (I have found it isn't)! You led me to a form of contraception I can feel relaxed and comfortable with.

No hard feelings,
Sarah, Germany

So. Contraception for people with vaginas. Weight gain, basal temperatures, mucus, copper up your cervix, links to depression ... fun! At this point in the book, you might be thinking, *It's the twenty-first century – why is there no contraception for people with penises (other than condoms)?!* Is there any real reason for this lack of medical development?

Yes, there are some reasons ...

WHAT ABOUT THE MEN?

First off, when I say 'male contraception', we're talking about birth control for folks with penises and testes. Not men. Just like how not all women have periods and not all menstruators are women, not everyone with a penis is a man and not all men have penises. Trans and non-binary folk exist! I'll use gender-inclusive language as much as possible, but most of the studies, news articles and companies working in this area use 'men' and 'male'. And as far as I know, the participants in those studies are cisgender men.

As we've seen, there are many contraceptive options available for the uterus-bearing population, but currently there are only two options for Team Testes: condoms and vasectomy. The former is a no-side-effects (if you're not allergic to latex), one-use-only barrier that you use every time you have sex. Pretty easy and non-invasive. The latter is literally surgery. The tubes are cut or sealed to prevent sperm in the testes from getting to the urethra and it's considered permanent (because it's very difficult to reverse). So, two wildly different, but both non-hormonal, options. One is very non-committal and the other, well, is a huge commitment – and there's nothing in between.

So why not?

Historically, contraception has been the burden of womb-owners. It's more important and vital to us as pregnancy and childbirth can be dangerous and even life-threatening.

The stakes are high. There is no such risk for the people providing the sperm – they will not die from pregnancy.

Another reason is the pure mechanics of it. We can stop one or two eggs per month, but 250 million sperm per ejaculation is another matter entirely. And since extremely effective and safe contraception already exists, anything new must meet the same high standards. That all being said though, it does just feel so bloody unfair. The burden we bear is not as simple as taking one pill a day or having a device put in once every five years. It's the constant thinking, worrying and planning that goes with it.

During a Q&A for a book event I was hosting, someone in the audience asked a question about why there isn't any viable male contraception when statistically men cause more pregnancies than women. I can see the logic in this thinking. Yes, it takes two to tango, but if I got pregnant today and carried it through until term, I would not be able to get pregnant for another nine months. But the person who got me pregnant? Who knows how many more pregnancies they could have caused in the same nine months. As mentioned, we vaginal vixens have a fertile window each month of about a week before and during ovulation. The rest of the time we can't get pregnant. But Team Testes is fertile *all the time.* There is no window.

That makes it seem like there could potentially be a huge number of pregnancies caused by just one person and their many different ejaculations. But it's not the case. The main reason being that for every one of these ejaculations, there would need to be an egg ready and waiting for it to cause a pregnancy. And in fact, most randomly timed acts of penis in vagina sex do not result in pregnancy. If you're into maths, statistics and fun hypothesizing, I would recommend Cordelia Fine's *Testosterone Rex*, especially the 'One Hundred Babies?' chapter.

So we can mostly let guys off the hook for that one. But the bitter truth is that within the patriarchy, an unwanted pregnancy has drastically more serious consequences for the pregnant person, not the sperm-carrier – so it's no wonder the responsibility of contraception has fallen on womb-bearers. But it's the twenty-first century! We can do better than that. It's time to share the load (by not sharing the load). Get it?

Trials and developments

There was a huge media splash at the end of 2016 when a trial for a male contraceptive injection was halted. It was reported that even though the injection was 96 per cent effective at preventing pregnancy, some men had dropped out of the study due to side effects such as acne and mood swings. Welcome to our world! Many people, myself included, as well as various 'hot takes' in the media ranted about the double standards and how men couldn't handle something that women have been dealing with for the last 60 years. But whilst society and medicine are not without their sexism and gender-based double standards, there is more to unpack here about why the trial was stopped.

320 men in monogamous relationships with women took part in the study by Professor Richard Anderson and were given injections every eight weeks; one injection contained

progestogen and the other testosterone. The study was halted by one of the committees monitoring the trial's safety because it was concerned by the high level of side effects reported. Apparently, the rate of side effects was higher than what women typically experience with their contraception, which is more effective than just 96 per cent. So the risk outweighed the benefits. Just under half of men reported acne as one of the side effects, whereas acne is reduced in 70 per cent of women who take the pill. We have much higher standards for contraception now than when the pill was first being developed sixty years ago (which can only be a good thing) and three-quarters of the men in the study did say that they wanted to continue taking the injection – most of the men didn't' wimp out' because of the side effects. So hopefully it's a good sign that we're on our way to having a contraceptive with fewer side effects and higher effectiveness that men can take.

There's also a male contraceptive pill in development and an injection that is like a reversible non-surgical vasectomy. A gel is injected into the tubes that carry the sperm from the testes to the urethra, which blocks sperm from passing through – it can potentially last years and another injection would dissolve the gel to let sperm pass through again. Even though I don't have a penis, this one sounds like my favourite; I'll be cheering it on from the sidelines.

Another method that is in development is a hormonal gel that is rubbed into the arms and shoulders daily. Apparently this male contraceptive product is the one furthest along in the development process and the closest to getting made, but we may still need to wait ten years. TEN YEARS?! Before looking into this, I genuinely believed we were maybe two or three years away from male contraception coming on to the market. Unfortunately, I was wrong.

Despite the fact that we're still years or possibly decades away from anything being available other than condoms and vasectomy, I am hopeful that now the work is being done, one day we'll have more balance amongst genders when it comes to contraceptive choices. Until then, best of luck to us all in finding the one for us.

Dear contraception for Team Testes,

It makes me laugh when I picture one day in the future when my boyfriend comes home from the chemist with a box of pill packets twice the size I've ever seen. The packaging is dark blue and black, the tablet is big and square and the very macho lettering reads 'THE PILL FOR MEN'. Or NHS leaflets in doctors' waiting rooms with the same blue-black colour scheme that say 'LARC – FOR MEN' or 'MAN-SIZE INJECTIONS'.

In all seriousness, I think the promotion will be better than that when you are finally available (at least I hope so!), but the idea of it makes me chuckle. Also, on a more selfish note, I just want to be a witness to this historic moment. Take your time with the trials to make sure you get everything right, but also hurry up because you are going to be an absolute game-changer. Another Big Deal.

See you soon (hopefully),

Hannah
X

PART THREE

Disorders, diseases and infections

There's no point in avoiding the issue: things can go wrong 'down there'. If you want a rundown of STIs, you can find that in my first book, *Doing It!*, but here we're tackling the non-sexually transmitted infections.

I know from making *The Hormone Diaries* series that a lot of people have various gynaecological conditions that affect them in different ways. The comments I received have opened my eyes to so many different experiences, and more of these stories need to be told. Not just so we all feel less alone and can have a moment of 'Oh my God, I get that too!', but also so we can be more understood by the people around us who don't share our experiences. There are a lot of heartbreaking stories of pain and years of misdiagnoses, but hopefully by empowering ourselves with knowledge and making a noise, things will change. People won't have to suffer in silence or fear or be in a complete state of confusion having no idea what's going on.

Just to remind you: I am an advocate and a communicator. I am not a doctor! This book cannot diagnose you. Even if you're currently struggling to get a diagnosis, please don't use this book to find one. Use it to learn about other people's experiences and stories. Use it to find the courage to go to the doctor. Use it to get inspired to try a different doctor. Use it to give yourself the language to talk about your body.

It's not my job to give you a complete list of everything that can go wrong down there, but I wouldn't advise you scour the internet for one either – unless you like scaring yourself – or to read those big daunting books that doctors use. Instead, we're going to talk about some of the most common issues and what that means for people's lived experiences and how they relate to their bodies. You can find an official medical breakdown elsewhere – this is about experiences and curiosity.

Some of these conditions I'd heard of before, such as UTIs, PCOS and endometriosis, but others I've only learned about in the last few years such as Turner syndrome and vaginismus. It can feel quite isolating if you have any of these conditions. With so little information out there and so few people talking about it, no wonder we are all constantly worried that our bodies aren't normal. And on top of the symptoms you have, there's the mental battle. Should I go to the doctors? What do I say to the doctor? Will they have to look at my bits? That's just the first hurdle. As you'll see, a very common experience is getting misdiagnosed, ignored, not taken seriously, or not getting diagnosed at all.

ENDOMETRIOSIS

Dear endometriosis,

Why are you straight up trying to ruin my life? Spending my whole life lying in bed with a hot water bottle to try and counteract the immense pain you cause is frustrating and no fun at all! Why is it that you always come back even though every surgeon assures me that 'This is the last surgery you'll have to have'?!

You're a selfish cow trying to take away my ability to contribute to society and live a full life, and I would prefer it if you went away. If you would just

If you have surgery, you may need it more than once if not all the endometriosis tissue was removed or if some of it grows back.

calm down and stop creating extra cells, all would be swell. Stop trying to be such an overachiever!

Regards,
Abbey, New Zealand

Endometriosis is a condition where the lining of the womb grows outside of the uterus in places such as the ovaries and fallopian tubes. This can cause back and stomach pains, extremely painful periods, heavy bleeding, pain during sex and fertility issues. It can seriously affect people's lives.

Notorious for being frequently misdiagnosed, the average wait time for an endometriosis diagnosis is currently seven to eight years. That's a ridiculous amount of time for a condition that roughly one in ten women suffer from! The uncertainty and confusion this causes can lead to anxiety and depression on top of the physical symptoms.

Dear fibroids and endometriosis,

It only took about six years of doctors' visits for someone to actually listen to me. For someone to realise there was a problem. Thank you for making my periods the worst week ever. The pain is real. The pain is very, very real. You suck.

Woohoo to finally be getting it sorted though! Not going to miss you.

Love,
Lily-Rose, UK

Since symptoms vary from person to person, and other conditions can cause similar symptoms, the only way to be certain you have endometriosis is to have a laparoscopy.

This keyhole surgery involves a camera being put in and around your insides to find out what's going on. The camera is in a thin tube that is fed through a small incision in your skin while you're under general anaesthetic. It's a very common procedure and usually you'll be able to go home the same day. The NHS doesn't exactly offer this procedure willy-nilly – hence why they run many other tests beforehand, and the likely reason endometriosis takes so long to diagnose. However, there may be some hope on the horizon – a blood test is being developed that can detect endometriosis in 90 per cent of cases. Hopefully, this will make waiting times for diagnosis much shorter.

Treatment

There is currently no cure for endometriosis but there is treatment available to help relieve the symptoms – depending on the type and severity of them, your age, if you want to get pregnant and how you feel about surgery.

* **Pain relief**
(paracetamol, ibuprofen)

* **Hormonal treatment**

* **Surgery**
(either a laparoscopy to destroy or remove endometriosis tissue or a hysterectomy, which is the removal of the womb and cannot be reversed.)

If you have been diagnosed with endometriosis, talk to your doctor to figure out the best course of action for you. Everyone's bodies and needs are different.

Dear endometriosis,

When I was 21 and I started getting cramps all month, I didn't know what I had in store from you, or what you were. I didn't know I'd go through years of pain and emotional stress trying to get someone to tell me what you were. For the first three years, the nurses told me the pain you put me in was just stress, that I had just had bad relationships, that it was in my head, that my irregular periods were 'normal', that I had vaginismus, that I had vulvodynia, that I had bacterial vaginosis, that I had any number of infections. I didn't. The therapist they sent me to was the one who referred me back for proper treatment.

It should not have been a therapist who told me that I had a real physical problem, it should have been one of the many, many doctors I saw. After three years I was told I had you, but would need laparoscopy surgery. Only after two of these failed ablation surgeries did I join an online forum that told me 40,000 women in my position were receiving substandard treatment, and learn that this was an under-researched disease that even general gynaecologists don't have training for. Yet,

it is as common as asthma. Even after my
third surgery I was still left in pain.
By that time I had tried most hormone
treatments: progestogen pills, the combined
pill, the coil, the implant and the injection,
not to much relief. I thought there might have
been something else going on, so I returned to
the doctor. And I was right. So ...

Dear adenomyosis,

I knew after my first
endometriosis surgery
that I still had a
problem with pain and
that it was difficult
to describe my uterus
literally hurting all
month, every day. I
knew doctors thought I
was crazy, so I had to
find out what you were
myself. I now know only
a hysterectomy will get
rid of you.

Adenomyosis and endometriosis
are different but similar conditions.
One does not cause the other,
Harriet just got extremely unlucky
and ended up with both. With
endometriosis, the uterus lining
can grow in the fallopian tubes
and ovaries, whereas adenomyosis
is a condition where the cells of
the lining of the womb are found
within the walls of the womb.

I still feel angry that nobody told me that
you existed and what your symptoms were. I
still feel angry that no one believed me. I
feel angry for all the women who have you, who
have no real treatment option. I feel angry
for the women who have received very bad care
for endometriosis, too. I feel angry for the
women who have been put on blanket treatments
while there is little research for a cure.

My heart aches when hearing these stories. I met someone recently who has a bladder pacemaker to help her pee because of her endometriosis. This is *serious*. But in society and the media, women's pain is treated differently to the pain suffered by men. Periods are a joke. PMS is a joke. And any kind of similar symptoms, even if they are more severe, are still seen as a joke. But it's not funny. We need to stop laughing and start listening.

Endometriosis is so common, and people are suffering physically and mentally because we can't get our shit together to take women's health and women's pain seriously. NICE, the National Institute for Health and Care Excellence, recently issued *groundbreaking* guidance for doctors on endometriosis. It said: 'Listen to women'. Apparently, that's all it takes.

UTIS

Dear UTIs,

You are so frustrating. You bring on that desperate feeling that I need to go to the toilet urgently, so I sit down, relax and … barely a few drops come out. I pull up my knickers, walk out the bathroom and WHAM there's the urge again. I can tell you're just toying with me. But I can't risk it. I can't just call your bluff and potentially wet myself. So every time I rush back to the loo and every time you're just a trickle. Rude.

I remember you reared your ugly head when I was 18 and on my way to a festival with my then-boyfriend and his friends. We stopped off at a supermarket for food, booze and … incontinence pads. So embarrassing. I drank so much water on the drive down that luckily you disappeared before we got to the festival – and thank you, but don't scare me like that again! It made me realise how much power you have, you could have completely ruined my weekend. A UTI at a festival, ugh. I am so sorry for anyone who you've ever tortured in that way, what did they do to deserve that? Anyway, I'm very glad there have been few signs of you in the last year.

Hannah
x

UTIs (urinary tract infections) aren't exactly to do with hormones, but are definitely related to our vulvas and are very common. Of the conditions mentioned in this part of the book, to my knowledge I've only ever had a UTI, but I've had many of them and it's not pleasant. You may experience one or a combination of different symptoms such as:

Needing to urgently pee all the time.

Stomach ache (mild to severe).

Pain or burning feeling when peeing.

Blood in your pee (this usually means your infection is severe).

Smelly or cloudy pee.

Sometimes I'll get a UTI that is just the pain – and oh boy, it hurts so much. You have to keep stopping the flow of pee to take deep breaths, recover and then release, preparing yourself for more pain. Other times, I get UTIs without pain but I'll have the urge to pee all the time. It's the most annoying, frustrating thing.

The urinary tract is your body's pee drainage system, and includes your kidneys, bladder and the tubes that connect them. UTIs are usually caused by bacteria (e.g. from poo) getting all up in there via the urethra (where your wee comes out). Anyone can get a UTI, but they are more common in folks with vulvas because our urethras are much shorter and closer to our anuses – so poo bacteria can get up in our urinary tract much faster.

As much as UTIs can feel like a constant but non-serious battle in our lives, do make sure you get them treated if they persist; left untreated, they can cause more serious problems, such as kidney infections or worse. If you experience feverish flu-like symptoms when you suspect you have or have had an infection (of any kind), call 111. Infections often clear up on their own, but if not, they can result in sepsis (poisoning of the bloodstream), which is life-threatening. If you are worried, describe your symptoms to the operator (and as much background info as you can) and they will let you know what's best to do.

When you go to your doctor's appointment, you'll need to give a urine sample so they can test it and confirm you have a UTI. Then they may prescribe you antibiotics. Make sure you finish the whole course of antibiotics even if your symptoms disappear beforehand. If you stop taking antibiotics too soon, the drug may not have killed off all the bacteria and the UTI could come back. This is also true for any other conditions that you may need to take antibiotics for. Finish your course!

Ways to avoid getting UTIs

Dear UTIs,

My worst memory of you is when my friend and I went to a festival for a day, a day in which I also happened to get my period. Having a UTI when the only available toilets are portaloos and there are thousands of other people waiting to use them is just not ideal. I think my bladder gave up by the end of the day, because when I got home I couldn't get my shorts off quickly enough, and peed myself, aged 18. Luckily, this gave me the kick I needed to get some antibiotics, and the scarring memory has been motivation enough to get me to pee after sex every single time since.

Oh no.

For solidarity reasons I'm going to tell you that I wet myself when I was 19. I was locked out of my friend's flat that I was supposed to be staying at. I had been drinking and I was desperate for the toilet. I wet myself on a street in Paris at 4 a.m. Not my proudest moment.

Love,
Natalie, UK

Pee after sex

Oh, how many times have I yelled this? Pee after having sex, people! You've got a lot of bodily fluids just messing around and hanging out together, bacteria flying left, right and centre. Having a good pee afterwards helps to just flush it all out.

Wipe front to back

It's embarrassing how old I was when I realised I'd been doing this wrong, and when you're so used to wiping one way, it's actually really difficult to teach yourself any different. It's a muscle memory so I had to completely relearn this daily habit, and I'm ashamed to say it took me a while. I was genuinely so embarrassed I didn't know you were supposed to wipe front to back that I didn't tell anyone. It seemed to me like everyone else had sussed this out in childhood and I had no idea I'd been doing it wrong all these years – no wonder I got so many UTIs! So I'm admitting this now for anyone who, like me, was much older when they learned this lesson or are maybe just learning it now. That's fine! There's nothing wrong with you! You're not a failure! It's our education and society that's failed us.

Fully empty your bladder when you pee

That's right. Shake it all out.

Don't hold in your pee for ages

When you gotta go, you gotta go. As soon as you feel the urge to pee, go as soon as you can.

Drink lots of fluids

Just great life advice in general. Drink water!

Cotton underwear

Hello, my name is Hannah. I'm 27 years old and I exclusively wear high-waisted cotton underwear. Turns out lacy knickers and girl boxers were just a phase, I have found my true calling now.

UTIs are probably the 'down-there' conditions we know most about and are least embarrassed to talk about. My takeaway from this is that anything to do with the urethra = fine, but anything to do with the vagina = bad. And even though they are next-door neighbours, one is considered a lot more shameful and more taboo than the other.

Dear UTI,

Okay, lesson learned. Sex in a lake is a bad idea. Sex in a lake during Bible camp is a really bad idea. Lakes are gross. Lake microbes in your urethra are grosser. Spending the next day vomiting non-stop is the grossest, and the trip to urgent care with your mother is the most awkward.

My bad.

Sincerely,
Tracy, USA

I'm sorry this happened to you, but you have to admit: it's very funny.

THRUSH

OK, this isn't a hormonal condition either but because it often appears together with a UTI, or in quick succession, I wanted to mention it. Thrush is a very pretty name for what is in fact a common yeast infection! Thrush is uncomfortable and tends to recur. You usually don't get it just once. Some people don't get any symptoms at all, but where there are symptoms, these include odourless white vaginal discharge that resembles cottage cheese (lunch anyone?), itching and irritation around the vagina, soreness and stinging during sex and when you pee. The vaginal discharge is what will distinguish thrush from a UTI. Which is another reason to regularly check your vagina and know what your normal discharge looks like (something it's a good idea to get into the habit of anyway).

Thrush can affect other areas of skin such as the armpits, groin and between the fingers. This manifests as a red, itchy or painful rash that is scaled over by white or yellow discharge and it is more noticeable on paler skin. It is generally treated with anti-fungal medicine prescribed by your doctor, although you can also talk to your local pharmacist about it, and it should be gone within a week.

I have never experienced thrush. I'm not sure how I have escaped this fate considering the amount of UTIs I've had. When I told some friends this, they were shocked – to them, thrush was a regular occurrence and wanted to know how I've managed to avoid it my entire life. But unfortunately, I have no idea – no tips or advice on how to avoid thrush. And to be honest, if I do ever get thrush, I feel so unequipped about how I would deal with it. I imagine I'll be calling up the same friends. 'What is happening to my vagina?! What do I do?!' Oh, how grateful I am that I can talk about these things with friends.

VAGINISMUS

I only learned that vaginismus was a thing a few years ago, and that's because a friend of mine was comfortable enough to share her experiences of it with me. It was completely new information to me, but my goodness, it explained a lot. I wish it was taught in schools as part of sex education. I can't even begin to explain how valuable it would be.

Vaginismus is the involuntary contraction of muscles which makes it really difficult or completely impossible to get anything inside the vagina. It's often described by people who have it as like punching a brick wall. *Nothing* is getting passed that. People who suffer with vaginismus may experience a lot of pain when having penetrative sex or may not be able to insert anything including a tampon.

Dear vaginismus,

Who knew you existed?! It's not something they teach you about in sex education, and because everyone tells you that your first time having sex will hurt, it's something that you shrug off the first few times. I got into a new relationship with the most amazing, caring guy and thought that maybe because I loved him so much I'd be able to overcome the pain for him. Of course, I was wrong. We tried to have sex and I had to stop him because of the excruciating pain and I had to explain to him all about my issue with sex. I felt like I was useless as a girlfriend (which I know now is far from true) and I felt like I would never be able to please a man.

It was my boyfriend who urged me to go to the doctor. The first doctor I went to see told me everything was normal and that this was normal for women. But I couldn't take that for an answer. The second doctor was surprisingly super-understanding. She knew that having pleasurable sex was healthy and important to me as a 20-year-old. She reassured me and explained she thought I had vaginismus. However, the waiting list she put me on for psychosexual therapy is over a year long, so now I'm taking matters into my own hands. I bought myself dilators and vibrators and after a few months they are starting to work – me and my boyfriend have managed to have sex for the first time pain-free and it feels like there's finally hope.

So, dear vaginismus, although you have been hell, thank you for teaching me to persevere and reminding me how strong I can be through times like these.

From,
Katie, UK

What causes vaginismus is a bit of a mystery, but one of the theories is that it's psychological. It could be triggered by a past sexual trauma, bad experiences with sex, painful medical conditions, growing up believing that sex is shameful and wrong, or just a general fear around sex or that your vagina is too small. Your vagina basically has a mind of its own and is clenching as a form of protection from danger: penises, tampons, fingers and beyond!

If you have vaginismus, you may be referred to therapy to help unpack your feelings and fears around penetration, but there is also physical treatment available. Pelvic floor exercises can help and you can get dilators or vaginal trainers that come in different sizes, starting small and gradually getting bigger, like Russian dolls. If you're in a relationship, it might also be a good idea to involve your partner in treatment so they can support you and know what's going on.

Dear vaginismus,

Screw you for reducing the sex I can AND want to have to about zero. Screw you for making the dating pool so small I literally cannot imagine finding anyone. Screw you for making me feel weird and broken and horrible. Screw you for making me think I wasn't good enough and that I had nothing to give to anyone. And screw you for making me so insecure that I would cry myself to sleep sometimes.

But also, thank you. For making me realise that sex can be so much more than penetration.

Thank you for showing me I can have amazing intercourse without any penetration. Thank you for being a filter for people who don't deserve me because if they cared about me, as a person, they would like me anyway. Thank you for being a douchebag-filter for friends. And thank you to my partner who supported me and made me feel so loved.

Elisabeth, Australia

At this point I'm going to confront our obsession with penetration. Penis in vagina (PIV) sex is seen as the holy grail of sex acts. The final base, the thing everyone refers to when they say, 'We did everything but ...' What society considers 'real sex'. BULLSHIT. Sex can be whatever you want it to be and can involve different things, not just penetration. Not to mention that sex for gay men usually doesn't involve vaginas and sex for gay women usually doesn't involve penises. So you can totally have a fulfilling sex life without PIV sex. But mentally, it may be hard not to think that your sex life could be ruined if you have vaginismus because of everything we've been taught about what 'real sex' is. I can't imagine how frustrating and upsetting it is not to be able to have PIV sex when you want to. But hopefully there is some comfort in the idea that there is LOTS of other sex that you can be doing that is fabulous, valid and REAL.

Dear vaginismus,

You made me feel like I was broken, because I thought my worth to boys revolved around whether they could put their penis in my vagina and have 'real sex'. You made me have conversations with boys that I didn't want to have and made me feel like it was my fault when our relationship would fall apart because of you. However, I now realise that in a weird way you were trying to protect me. The help I'm receiving lets me see that it wasn't any more my fault suffering from you than it was having a period. Thank you for helping me realise that I am more than my ability to have PIV sex.

Love,
Laura, UK

PCOS (POLYCYSTIC OVARY SYNDROME)

Dear PCOS,

You made your first appearance when I was 13 – nice timing, thanks for that. You made my life hell, making me feel different, giving me acne, excess hair, dark patches of skin that made people think I didn't bathe regularly, painful periods that would arrive without warning (if they ever arrived), endless doctors' appointments and not knowing if I will be able to have children.

But eight years have now passed and I no longer hate or fear you. You are a part of me that I completely accept, which means you no longer control me or my life. You have made me grow as a person, learn to accept help and support from those around me and have given me the opportunity to be part of a wonderful community of strong women. I wear my teal-coloured ribbon with pride.

All my love,
Sophie, UK

As part of *The Hormone Diaries* video series, I sat down with a friend who has PCOS to talk about her experience with it. What we learned from a quick read of the NHS page was that PCOS (polycystic ovary syndrome) affects about one in five women in the UK. And confusingly, despite the 'cystic' bit in its name, PCOS doesn't mean you actually have cysts on your ovaries. What?! It's funny how you can have a condition for most of your life but still not really understand the hows and the whys.

So, what are polycystic ovaries if they aren't cysts on your ovaries? People with PCOS usually have enlarged ovaries containing follicles, which are fluid-filled sacs that surround the eggs. So it all happens on the *inside* of the ovary, not the outside. Since the eggs are all wrapped up in follicle cocoons, they often fail to release, meaning ovulation doesn't occur. That's why one of the symptoms of PCOS is difficulty getting pregnant (though with treatment it is possible). However, confusingly, it's possibly to have polycystic ovaries without having PCOS, and it's possible to have PCOS without having polycystic ovaries, if you have other symptoms such as irregular periods or excess hair.

Dear PCOS,

Because of you I eat better, work out harder, drink more water and no longer give a monkeys about the hair on my face! You have cost me money on laser treatments, private doctors and medication, but I wouldn't want you gone. You make me fitter, healthier, STRONGER. You're a pain, but I don't want you to go.

Lily, UK

There are other things going on with PCOS too, such as bodies producing excess androgens, which are the 'male hormones', including testosterone. This may have physical effects such as increased facial or body hair. If you have PCOS, your periods may be irregular because you're not releasing eggs regularly, and you may experience other symptoms such as weight gain and difficulty losing weight, oily skin, and head-hair loss or thinning.

Dear PCOS,

These cramps and the hair growth can do one.

Ellen, UK

Society is full of gender norms, pressures and expectations. For women, that can include being a baby-making machine, having little to no body hair and being slim – all of which are potentially affected by having PCOS. I'll say it again – one in five women have it! Women come in all shapes and sizes and all bodies are valid and deserve respect. What is deemed by society as 'normal' and 'acceptable' can leave people with conditions like PCOS feeling like they don't fit in or that they're not good enough in some way. Obviously, this is hogwash.

Dear PCOS,

Thank you for instilling tenacity in me. If you weren't so mysterious and elusive, I never would have had to learn to assert myself and make my views heard. Also, thanks for the acne and the weight, because it took having them for me to learn not to give a shit. Also, the beard is low-key dope.

Thanks for everything,
Laura, USA

There's a model of understanding the disabled community uses that I think can also be applied to other situations, including this one. It's called the Social Model of Disability, and it states that it is not a person's condition that disables them, but rather society through inaccessibility and stigma. So it is not PCOS that makes someone less of a woman, it's society's definition of 'woman' that might make someone feel that way.

Dear PCOS,

I may not like that you're a part of my life, but I'm so happy to have found out you exist. After years of heavy, painful and irregular periods, to have found out I wasn't just 'blowing things out of proportion' was amazing. As women, I think we are told a lot that our periods are normal when they might not be.

You make it almost impossible to lose weight. You've made me have increased chances of having a health problem like diabetes or heart disease. You've given me more body hair than I would like.

But you've also made me realise I'm not crazy and there is actually a problem with my body that can be helped. Thanks to you, PCOS, I've now met the mini-pill and so far my problems seem to have lessened. Yes, the periods still exist and still last weeks, but they are lighter — it's better than feeling like my womb is trying to escape my body every month.

Lots of love,
Georgia, UK

Although there is no cure for PCOS, there are ways to treat the symptoms. A lot of people go on the pill to help balance out the hormones, but as we've discovered, hormonal contraception isn't for everyone. For some people, the symptoms of PCOS can be unwanted and extremely distressing – in that case, go to your doctor to see what your options are, and join PCOS support groups online to see what has worked for others. But if the symptoms don't really bother you, that's fine too – you don't have to have any treatment. You don't have to go on the pill if you don't want to; you don't have to try to lose weight if you don't want to (it's harder to lose weight when you have PCOS, so you might find the lack of 'results' discouraging anyway); you don't have to shave or take medication for hair growth if you don't want to. Your body, your decision!

Dear PCOS,

Thank you. I was having a rough time with dysphoria when I found out about you, and I really needed the answers I finally got when I was told I had high testosterone.

Thank you. I needed some spare weight when I was going through the roughest parts of my eating disorder, and to feel that severe restriction wasn't going to work anyway.

Thank you. I needed to learn to be more conscious of what I was eating when my symptoms turned to binges and my weight got dangerously high.

Thank you. I developed more independence stepping out of my comfort zone to schedule appointments and blood tests and ultrasounds about you.

Thank you. I finally have something to explain where my depression, anxiety, facial hair, acne, thin hair and mild insulin issues stem from.

Thank you. I'll be real with you, it's been a blessing to only have five periods a year.

Thank you. I'm glad I might be infertile because I don't experience sexual attraction and I know I don't ever want kids, so if something awful ever happens to me, there's less chance that I'll have to go through a tough decision.

Thank you. I have chronic fatigue

I hadn't heard of a connection between PCOS and chronic fatigue before, but it's a thing. Fatigue isn't a symptom of PCOS but people with PCOS are potentially at a higher risk of getting chronic fatigue. There isn't a lot of information out there about this, so go to your doctor to get answers to any questions.

because of you, but that's helped me prioritise what's important to me, and to stop spending energy on things I don't actually want or need to do.

Much love,
Leigh, Australia

THE LIST GOES ON ...

The rest of the conditions that I'm going to talk about are ones we had diary entry submissions for, but there are so many other health issues out there so this is by no means a finite list. For example, there are different cancers you can get in the ovaries, cervix, uterus, vulva and vagina, and there are other things that aren't cancer, such as vulvodynia (pain in the vulva area), bleeding during/after intercourse, PID (pelvic inflammatory disease) and a whole host of STIs we haven't gone into in this book. If you're ever in pain or notice something out of the ordinary for you and your body, make note of it and book yourself a GP appointment. It might be nothing, it might be something. But like most things, if it is something, then the earlier you go to get checked out and treated, the better.

Ovarian cysts

Dear ovarian cyst,

It would be really great if I could get through life never experiencing you again. I've had a child and the pain of you bursting is right up there with labour pains, and at least childbirth has a positive result. Fingers crossed that you stay away.

Sincerely,
Caitlin, Canada

A baby, a.k.a.
a positive result.

We talked about how PCOS isn't actually having cysts on your ovaries, but ovarian cysts are definitely a thing. I just searched for 'cysts' without specifying 'ovarian', and the first result showed an image of some under-the-skin cysts (basically like huge spots) and I was simultaneously grossed out but also got the urge to squeeze them.

Ovarian cysts are fluid-filled sacs that hang out on your ovaries (maybe just on one ovary, maybe both). They're common and usually don't cause any symptoms – they just naturally come and go. Who knows, maybe I've had many an ovarian cyst and I've never known because mine have never caused me issues? But sometimes they can lead to problems – if they burst or they're really big or somehow stop the blood supply to your ovary (which doesn't sound good).

It's worth noting that most ovarian cysts are benign, but some can be cancerous and there is a bigger chance of this for people who have gone through menopause. It's always worth getting checked out if you're experiencing any kind of pain or other symptoms. There are different levels of monitoring and treatment depending on the severity of the situation, but most cysts will disappear on their own after a few months.

This is a long and hilarious story about an ovarian cyst that I just had to include because it makes me chuckle every time I read it!

Dear ovarian cysts,

Before I start reminiscing, I just want to say first that I have a dark sense of humour and secondly that some parts of the story may seem sad but they need to be, because it makes the story even more awkward and hilarious.

So, a few years ago I had this pain just above my left hip joint, but because I was about to start my period that month, I thought nothing of it and assumed it was just an odd cramp. At the time my auntie was in a hospice in palliative care, so me and my parents were there every day with my cousins. Because my mind was focusing on that, I wasn't paying attention to my stomach/vagina/that part of my body. My period had been stopped for a while but I was still having sharp internal pains and I didn't know why. Every step I took on my leg felt like someone was stabbing me in the gut, but it was only on my left side. I immediately thought, OH GOD, it's only on one side of my body — maybe it's my appendix? *That thought soon left my mind when my dad said, 'Mate, the appendix is on the right.'*

One day after coming home from the hospice, the pain got worse, walking was horrendous, and I had to crawl up the stairs. My brain thought, Well, when I have a crappy period cramp, a hot bath helps, so I ran a bath and gingerly stepped in. Then, trying to get out the bath, I couldn't lift myself up because the pain was unbearable, so I had to shout for my mum to help me out. As I stepped out of the bath I felt (and think I heard) this pop, like when you pop bubblegum, but it came from inside me.

The pain just got worse and my mum drove me to A & E at midnight. However, being a Friday night, the waiting room was full of drunk people from nights out who had fallen in their heels or got in a fight. I had a long wait, and when I was seen, they said it might be a cyst. I was booked in a few days later to have an ultrasound.

The day came, and my mum went to the hospice to look after my cousins, leaving my dad to take me to the hospital. There were dad jokes galore, which didn't help because every time I laughed, it really bloody hurt. I thought it'd just be an ultrasound like they do for babies. Well, I was wrong. The nurse said it was an internal examination up my vagina and AS SOON as that was said I ordered my dad away to the waiting room and he left, laughing at how embarrassed I was. I had the ultrasound, and the equipment basically looked like a sex toy. It was a bit uncomfortable but didn't hurt, and the nurse and doctor were chatting away to me the whole time.

When it was time for the results, I made my dad wait outside again because I didn't want him to hear about my vagina. The doctor told me there was a cyst, but that it had ruptured (most likely from the trauma of getting out of the bath tub). And THEN the doctor said, 'So it'd be best if you don't partake in sexual activities for a week or two whilst you heal up. I know your partner in the waiting room might not be chuffed, but you have to heal.' My face went red, my jaw dropped. She thought the guy in the waiting room was my partner ... *bleeguhh*. I spluttered, 'Woah – that's my dad, oh my God'. The poor doctor, her face went even redder than mine and she started apologising. I felt sorry for her but internally I was screaming EWWWW. She kept flapping about and then blurted out, 'WELL ... UMM ... you have a very lovely womb and a GREAT vulva!' My eyes just widened.

The doctor saw me out and when my dad looked up, he waved and smiled at the doctor, who promptly ran into her office. I waited to tell *him what had happened until we were sat in the car. I rang my mum to tell her the tale at the same time, laughing at how bizarre it all was. My mum kept quiet the whole time, and when I finished, she said three words that were the cherry on top of my weird day: 'You're on loudspeaker ...' Everyone in the room at the hospice (which included my auntie and uncle, my cousins, a nurse and my mum) had heard about my dad being my boyfriend, my lovely vulva and the dildo that was shoved up my vagina. GREAT.*

So, to my ovarian cyst, you showed up at a really inconvenient time. You made me so embarrassed, you made people think my dad was my boyfriend, and you really bloody hurt. But you did make a room of people going though a shitty time laugh and took their mind off things for a while — so thanks, I guess?

But please don't come back any time soon.

Ellie, UK

Turner syndrome

I learned about Turner syndrome from one of my viewers, who emailed me when I first starting posting *The Hormone Diaries* videos. I'd never heard of it before, because it is quite rare, but I wanted to touch on it since it's pretty different to some of the other conditions we've talked about. Around one in two thousand baby girls are born with Turner syndrome, which is an abnormality with sex chromosomes. Instead of having two X chromosomes, people with Turner syndrome have one, with the other either missing or altered. Common symptoms are short stature and underdeveloped ovaries. This means that people with Turner syndrome may have a lack of periods and experience fertility problems.

Dear Turner syndrome,

We have been together since before I was born and I have known your name since I was able to understand that you were the thing that made me different. You made me self-conscious in school, because no one had heard of you. You were the reason I visited an endocrinologist so often, and because of you I have been on various hormones since the age of ten. First growth hormone to add height, then oestrogen, finally on to the combination pill (the one I still take to this day). I like to see the humour and shades of grey in life, and the idea of being an infertile woman who takes 'birth control' certainly has its irony. But of course, they are just female hormones my body does not produce on its own. Without them, I would be at risk of osteoporosis, and perhaps other issues such as heart disease. So taking these pills daily (with breaks of about a week every couple of months) has become second nature after almost twenty years.

I'm not bitter, TS, I think you still have a lot to teach me. You make me wonder what it would be like to have a body that produced these hormones on its own, that started menstruating – really menstruating, not just withdrawal bleeding from a drop in oestrogen and progestogen – signalling a possibility of creating life.

Even though I am still working on my self-esteem, I think we'll make it through this. After all, we have come this far.

Kate, Canada

A lot of people aren't diagnosed with TS until puberty. But once they are, they will have regular health checks and preventative care in relation to their hearing and ears, blood pressure, the thyroid gland, glucose levels and bone mineral density. Growth hormone therapy is also available as daily injections from the ages of around five to sixteen. Another treatment is oestrogen and progesterone hormone replacement therapy, because the ovaries do not work properly to produce their own. A minority of people with Turner syndrome can conceive naturally but may need assistance with IVF. And therapy may also be offered if needed for any psychological problems that may develop because of the condition.

Dear Turner syndrome,

It has been 15 years since you came into my life at the age of 14. You announced yourself when my periods stopped about six months after they had begun. It is almost impossible to explain the feeling of knowing you have effectively started the menopause before you have even fully gone through puberty — and watching all your friends grow and develop and go through things which are unattainable to you. It is even more difficult to get your head around the fact that your ovaries have given up the ghost and biological children will not be part of the life plan. Try dealing with that emotional rollercoaster on top of GCSEs and A Levels!

I have happily been on the combination pill all these years, which hasn't given me much to complain about, as well as thyroxine for my underactive thyroid (thanks for the stunted growth). With trepidation, I am about to embark on HRT since it's not recommended to stay on the pill indefinitely. I can only hope that I will find the same success with it, even if it takes some trial and error first.

The trickiest stage is now rearing its head — I am at an age where all my friends will be starting families very soon and I will have to smile and sit by while they go about their lives. I can only hope that one day I will be blessed with a family of my own through other means.

Becky, UK

In writing and researching this part of the book, I've realised that so many different conditions present in nearly identical ways and that one condition may cause the symptoms of another to occur. Obviously, research, diagnoses and treatment in this whole area need to improve, but part of me isn't surprised it's such a puzzle to figure out. If someone is experiencing pelvic pain, that could mean so many different things: ovarian cysts, endometriosis, PMDD ... the list goes on! But even if it takes years for a diagnosis (seriously, this needs to change), it'll be worth it to get to the bottom of it – the only way to know for sure what's up with your body is by going to the doctor.

GOING TO THE DOCTOR

If you need professional medical help or advice about something to do with your body, but feel a bit embarrassed talking about your private parts with a complete stranger, let this guide help and reassure you.

You're most likely to make your appointment via phone call and the person you speak to may well ask, 'What's this about?' You don't need to go into the back story of your symptoms and why you're booking an appointment – one sentence will suffice. Keep it to the point and if you're nervous, just write it down in advance, using words you might use to describe it to a friend.

Congratulations, you've booked an appointment! On the day, if it makes you feel more comfortable, you could bring someone you trust with you, who can join you for the appointment or just stay in the waiting room and be supportive. And remember, you are allowed to go the doctor by yourself when you're under 16, so you don't have to tell your parent/carer if you don't want to.

You're only going to have about ten minutes with a doctor, so you need to make the most of that time. Preparation is key.

1. Write down everything that's bothering you, including frequencies of symptoms and when they started (if you can remember). Use this to make sure you cover everything you want but also to help you with saying words such as 'vagina', 'vulva' and 'sex' out loud. It's much easier if you're just reading what you've already written down.

2. Remember, doctors have heard and seen it all. The only person in the room who's potentially embarrassed is you. The doctor literally doesn't care about you saying the word 'vagina'.

3. Start with the thing that is bothering you the most. Your doctor is likely to ask some follow-up questions, so if you start with the most pressing issue, you know you're covered if the questions go on for a long time.

4. Dress for the occasion! This sounds like very strange advice in this context, but hear me out. You may need a physical examination where you'll lie down and the doctor will take a look and feel inside. Wear whatever you'll feel most comfortable in. If wearing certain underwear will help you relax, then go for it! Slip-on shoes are easier to take off. And if you are a wearer of skirts, wear a skirt to the appointment. That way you can keep it on and fold it up instead of taking your whole bottoms off. Personally, it makes me feel like I'm less naked and vulnerable if the skirt is still around my waist.

It's worth mentioning that there may be times when instead of making an appointment with your GP, you should get yourself straight to A & E at a hospital. Such as when you have flu-like symptoms at the same time as a UTI, or like our dear friend Ellie and her ovarian cyst. If you're unsure if you should go to A & E, you can always call 111 to get guidance on what to do.

Maybe you can relate to some of the stories in this chapter, maybe you've learned something or maybe you have another condition that most people (including myself) have never heard of. Maybe you're building up the courage to go to the doctors after months or years of the same nagging symptoms you don't think are a 'a normal part of being a woman', maybe you've been to the doctors and you're still waiting for a correct diagnosis. Whatever your situation, I think we can all agree that it can be a bit confusing. Where is the line between 'normal' and 'probably should go to the doctor'? No two people are the same, but I hope it's been helpful to hear other people's stories to relate to and find comfort.

PART FOUR

Hormones and being trans

I really wanted to include a section on the experiences of trans people because trans people have their own unique hormone diaries to tell. Being transgender means that the sex you were assigned at birth does not match your gender. The opposite of this is cisgender, where your assigned sex does match your gender. I'm cis because the doctor saw my baby vulva, said, 'It's a girl!' and I am a girl. But that is not the case for everyone.

Transgender is a huge umbrella term that encompasses so many different identities and experiences. Some people might be binary trans people, which means they were AFAB (assigned female at birth) but they are a man, or they were AMAB (assigned male at birth) but they're a woman. For each individual, the transition from the sex you were assigned to the gender that you are is varied. Some may dress differently, go on hormones, have surgery, change their name and pronouns, wear make-up, not wear make-up, shave or not shave. There are many different ways to transition and it's not like a checklist you have to complete. If you're a trans woman, you're a woman; if you're a trans man, you're a man – you don't have to outwardly change anything for that to be true. However, many trans folks do use a variety of methods in their transition in order to feel more comfortable and less dysphoric in their body. Gender dysphoria describes the distress and discomfort that someone may feel because their assigned sex does not match their gender. But gender dysphoria is not a prerequisite to being trans; some trans people don't experience dysphoria.

Dear body,

I often feel disconnected from you. I try to avoid you. I shy away from your reflection. When they told me my flat chest would grow, when they told me I would have to change as my body changed, I prayed to God to keep you shapeless. I prayed that I could hide you, I prayed I could be left alone. When they said my actions and my feelings had to match the vagina you had and the breasts you would have, I was lost. When you changed, when I could no longer hide you, when others began to be uncomfortable by your presence, I could no longer ignore you. Before you grew, before you changed, I was just me. Now I am you, and that is all they see.

Each month I have discomfort in not just you, but me. I no longer just want to hide you – I want to hide myself. You have caused me ridicule, shame and hatred. You have shackled me. When you bleed, I am reminder of how I am wrong and gross.

But some days you are beautiful. It is not you I am mad at, it's the world for expecting me to understand you, and match you, that has caused the turmoil. You are me, no matter the disconnect. I am proud that we are different, I am proud we are complicated, I am proud to be housed in your shell.

I love you, but you do not dictate my gender, my way of life or my identity. You are just you, and together we make up me.

Kris, USA

Another useful term is non-binary. The 'binary' here is describing the genders as only male/female or man/woman. But some people do not identify as men or women. Non-binary can be an identity in itself, and it is also an umbrella term for anything and everything in the middle of the binary or outside of it completely. Specific terms include gender-queer, gender-fluid, agender, gender-variant, neutrois … the list is almost endless. There could be as many genders as there are people in the world. If you want a glossary of terms and explanations of them, I would highly recommend the book *The ABCs of LGBT* by Ash Hardell, a queer, non-binary YouTuber who also wrote a piece in my first book *Doing It!* about identity and labels. Non-binary folks may also choose to transition in any of the ways I mentioned earlier.

Dear fallopian tubes,

After years of trying different forms of contraception, I finally put you in shackles. Literally. Not even a week ago I had a tubal ligation, where they put a tiny camera and instruments into my body through my belly button and put titanium and silicone clips on you. You are still a little bit pissed and let me feel that from time to time. And mates, I totally get it. But it's the only solution. You are literally programmed to do one thing, a thing I do not want to experience. But come on, even though you are tied up, you can still do your thing. There's still gonna be periods. Only now I don't have to worry if my usually very-on-time period is a day late.

Just think of all the worry-free sex we're gonna have! Think about all the fun, about a lifetime of being relaxed and not having to worry about broken condoms or other stuff. Sure, we could still contract an STI if the condom breaks (and that would suck). But honestly, most of them are cured much more easily than *whispers* being pregnant. I suggest you accept your new accessories and we'll talk again in a few weeks.

FYI, I'm non-binary, but my gender doesn't have anything to do with not wanting kids. Plenty of enbies do want them.

Cheers,
JD, Austria

Enbies = NBs = non-binary people

There is no definitive data on how many transgender people there are in the UK, but the number is on the rise because of the increased visibility of trans people and a general shift to a broader understanding of gender. If you're not trans, I encourage you to learn about these issues and support trans people in whatever way you can.

Dear reproductive system,

It seems that you don't want to be inside my body any more than I want you to be in there! I have endometriosis and adenomyosis, along with chronic ovarian cysts. It took a decade for me to finally receive those diagnoses. It essentially means that I have endometrial tissue inside the walls of my uterus (where it shouldn't be) and also outside of my uterus.

As a trans person who is very dysphoric about having a uterus and getting periods, it's hard to cope. I joke that my reproductive system is destroying itself, because it shouldn't be inside me in the first place! I haven't found any relief through traditional birth control, so I will eventually need a hysterectomy.

I wish that feminist circles included us more (specifically trans-masculine people, non-binary trans folks and trans men), not just trans women and trans femme folks. I suffer from uterus and ovary-specific illnesses that are subject to sexist and transphobic healthcare rules and laws. My uterus is also still under the control of cisgender, straight white men in our government and I was raised as a 'girl', so I've been a victim of sexism in our society up until I came out – and sometimes I STILL am, because I'm misgendered constantly.

It's hard being a non-binary trans person in a world full of many transphobic, (strictly) binary, cisgender people. Let's ALL make an effort to be more inclusive, in our language surrounding periods (don't say 'feminine hygiene products' or 'a woman's time of the month'), uterus/ovaries/breast tissue-specific illnesses, and birth control! It makes a *huge* difference for people like me, who are non-binary transgender, and it's not difficult to do.

Masen, USA

Amen! These are such good points. There is fierce debate in feminist circles around trans issues at the moment but they mostly focus on trans women. All trans and non-binary folks should be supported by feminism; we shouldn't be excluding anyone as we're all marginalised by the same power structures. Oh hi, patriarchy.

In September 2020, Relationships and Sex Education (RSE) is currently scheduled to become compulsory in primary and secondary schools in England. This is a great opportunity to teach young people about gender and gender identity in an inclusive, accepting way and I fervently hope that content in RSE relating to minority groups such as LGBTQ+ students is woven throughout the curriculum, not just tagged on as an after-thought. Even if they're not out yet, young trans people need to see themselves reflected in what they're being taught. And it's good for the straight and cis kids in class to be aware of these things too. This is what I am trying to do with this book. I've included diary entry submissions from trans people in the other parts of the book because – guess what – some trans people have periods and some are on contraception. And we can't assume that all of the entries where the person's gender isn't specified are written by cis people. However, I also wanted to dedicate a whole chapter to trans people because there are some things that are specific to their experiences, such as hormone replacement therapy (HRT).

HORMONE REPLACEMENT THERAPY

Dear oestrogen,

I'm so grateful for having you in my life, finally. But God do you make me an emotional wreck! And growing up under the constraints of toxic masculinity, I am just not used to crying this much. Or feeling so much. I'm loving everything else about you, HRT, but please — chill out for five minutes?!

Hannah, UK

HRT was first invented to relieve menopausal symptoms. It replaces the hormones (oestrogen and progesterone) that are lowered during menopause to make it as smooth and easy a transition as possible. HRT is still used this way (and more on menopause later), but it's also taken by some trans people too. Trans women may take oestrogen and testosterone-blockers, and trans men may take testosterone, sometimes called T. Non-binary folk might also want to take a form of HRT. Just like with puberty, development happens at different rates, in different intensities for different people.

These are some of the common changes for those who take oestrogen:

Weaker growth of facial and body hair.

Fat distributed on hips.

Penis and testicles may get smaller.

Small breasts may develop.

Erections and orgasm may be harder to achieve.

Muscle loss.

Dear wonderfully amazing oestrogen,

How I love thee. Almost two years ago you were introduced into my life, a beautifully pink little pill. Twice daily I ingest you and I never miss a day. I need you so much.

Oh, the things you are doing to my body. My mind. My emotions. You have given me an inner calm that I never had before. Together with 'coming out', you have removed the inner anger that was contained within. I was angry at the world and everyone in it. You have helped to make me happy.

You are filling out my body in all the right places. I now have hips and a booty. A tummy — I love my tummy. And I have breasts. Wonderful breasts. Thank you. I love the way you are changing my face. That square jawline is now softened. Rounded. Like my cheeks. I look in the mirror and it excites me to see the changes you are making to my body.

My skin. Gone is that coarseness. You have made my skin ever so soft to the touch, so smooth. It feels amazing. You have also made the hair on my skin much thinner. In some places you have removed it altogether. Thanks for the smaller bladder now too. Not sure I wanted that, but hey, part and parcel right!

My emotions. What have you done to those …? At the first sign of something sad, you make me cry. You connect me with my inner humanity more than ever before. You have also changed the way I operate sexually. No longer is it all visual and physical, but mental too.

Oestrogen, thank you for coming into my life. Much love for everything you have done and for bringing me closer to the woman I always was. I look forward to our continued relationship.

Candice, Australia

Different changes will happen at varying rates for different people who take testosterone too, but here are some common changes:

Stronger growth of facial and body hair.

Clitoris may increase in size.

Libido may increase.

Deepening voice.

Periods are likely to stop.

Muscle gain.

Dear testosterone,

Thank you. Thank you for deepening my voice, for making me hairier, for changing my body fat distribution. Thank you for stopping my periods (and all the physical and emotional pain that came with them). Thank you for making my face look more masculine. Thank you for letting me embrace my femininity without sacrificing the way others perceive me. Thank you for increasing my self-confidence. Thank you for the acne that I don't really want but that I can learn to love, the way I've learned to love the rest of myself.

I can't explain the relief I felt after testosterone started changing my body. After 14 years feeling wrong, finally something felt right. Switching from injections to gel was another relief. My mind and soul have eased and grown. My outer appearance matches how I feel inside. Every day I'm closer to being my own dream boy.

Thank you testosterone, for everything.

With much gratitude,
Jake, Canada

This is by no means a complete list, and it mostly refers to physical changes – but we know that hormones can affect our mood too. In a video episode of *The Hormone Diaries*, trans

YouTuber Alex Bertie described to me how he found it much harder to cry when he started taking testosterone. There are so many potential changes that can happen to your body, and one person's experience won't be exactly the same as the next. And there may even be some changes you didn't expect, like the crying thing.

Most trans people undergo hormone therapy once they're an adult and finished with puberty, but many will know their true gender way before then, so the changes they go through during puberty can be a really distressing time. Hormone blockers can be prescribed to younger people to delay the effects of puberty to give the person more time before going on HRT or having any surgeries. You can get treatment on the NHS, but the waiting lists are often extremely long (up to two years). And a lot of treatment options aren't available until you're over 18 unless you have parental consent. There is private care, but that can be very expensive. Hundreds of pounds for appointments and consultations and thousands, even tens of thousands of pounds, for various gender-affirming surgeries.

MANSTRUATION

As mentioned right at the beginning of this book, not all women have periods and not all people who have periods are women. Even with HRT and surgeries, trans women will never have periods. But some trans women report getting some very familiar PMS symptoms: bloating, cramps, sore chest, nausea and mood swings. However, there is little research on this phenomenon (no surprises there), so we don't know if it's a direct result of taking HRT or a psychological thing. On the other hand, AFAB people who might be men or non-binary can still experience periods. Taking testosterone will alter your menstrual cycle and many people on T find that it stops their periods completely, but how long it takes and the regularity of periods in the meantime will vary from person to person. I've heard people calling it 'manstruation' instead and I really love that.

For some cis women, having periods is awful – mine were pretty moderate and even I went on contraception because I couldn't handle some of it. But for AFAB trans folks, you don't 'only' have to deal with the period, the bleeding, figuring out the best products to use and suffering from a variety of PMS symptoms. You have to do all that knowing how gendered periods are presented as – that they're a 'woman' thing, that getting your period is your first big step into womanhood, that it's a girls-only experience. And there's the added difficulty of using public toilets to change period products, since male toilets often don't have the privacy or the bins required to dispose of products.

Dear period,

You came when I was 12. I had no idea what was happening to me, I freaked out. I thought I was sick, but my school nurse told me it was natural. 'It's only your period, it happens to all girls.' I was even more confused; if only girls got their period, then why did I get it? I was turning into a mutant.

I tried to hide you, stealing pads from my mum and finding excuses to go to the nurse's office every time it happened. I managed to hide it for almost six months, but eventually my mum noticed the pads disappearing and talked to me. She was all giddy and excited of course, and I had to force a smile. But at fourteen, I couldn't take it any more. I had read that if you're underweight, your period disappears – so I stopped eating.

I spent three years variously skipping meals and throwing up, and my period didn't appear once. But I was tired of the constant fatigue, of looking like a skeleton, of not having any energy; I wanted to live again. So I started eating, a lot. I believed in the phrase 'Go big or go home' and I stuffed my face till I was ready to pop. I gained 7 kg within the first month, and then 13 kg more over the next six months. It still took almost a year for my period to come back, and for a while I thought it never would, and I was ecstatic.

Of course, when my body had been at a healthy weight for a while it came back, and what I now know is called gender dysphoria appeared all over again. Aged 19 I still haven't started hormones, and my period comes every. Damn. Month. Dear period, you are the reason I developed an eating disorder, you are the reason for a lot of pain and suffering in my life, you are the reason I lost some very good friends.

Now, since guys aren't even supposed to have periods, could you very kindly just sod off?

Mike, Norway

If you're not a woman, having a period can be a really traumatising experience. And that shouldn't be taken lightly. Trans people go through a boatload of stress because of hormones – if they choose to receive HRT, they'll basically go through puberty twice. Or imagine going through puberty that either costs you loads of money or lots of time waiting whilst you don't feel like you and you're also being harassed, chastised or ignored by many people and the media. To the trans and non-binary people who watch my videos and read my books: I see you. Thank you for sharing your stories with me; I learn so much from you and I'll try my best to support you, listen and care. You are incredible, wonderful, strong powerhouses and so many people see that.

PART FIVE

Pregnancy

There is a lot of information out there about pregnancy and motherhood. I've never been pregnant or a mother, but I do know that I want to be someday. When that time comes around, I'll be reading all the books, watching all the YouTube videos and listening to all the podcasts to get some kind of understanding of what on earth is happening. A woman I follow on YouTube had a baby last year. I was watching her videos about naturally inducing labour and in the video she said something like, 'If you're watching this, you're probably pregnant.' Nope. Not me. I'm just curious and fascinated by the whole thing.

Even if you receive absolutely no sex education in school, chances are you know about reproduction from biology lessons. Where babies come from, sperm, egg, embryo, foetus, pregnancy, etc. This is the 'acceptable' face of sex education because it's not about sexual pleasure, it's about making babies.

BREAKING NEWS: these days you don't even have to have sex to get pregnant. You can have sex without getting pregnant and you can get pregnant without having sex.

For some reason, my school thought it was important to make a class of 13-year-olds watch a graphic video of a woman giving birth. I guess you could call it a very effective method of contraception because I'm pretty sure we were all scarred afterwards. Yes, I know it's meant to be the miracle of life and all, but it's a very terrifying miracle of life. I'll tell you now, I am shit-scared of labour. Whenever I see people with kids passing me on the street, my brain tells me, *She did it, so can you. She did it, so can you.* It's like a mantra I have to tell myself.

I noticed a strange thing when I came off the pill, although I'm not sure if it was just a self-fulfilling prophecy. Ever since I was a kid, I'd always really wanted to be a mother, desperate to have babies and excited to know the feeling of being pregnant. But then I got a bit older and I stopped being so broody. I don't know if it was because I went on the pill or because I learned about feminism – and by 'learned about feminism', I don't mean that being a mother is not feminist, but rather that I internalised a lot of guilt around *wanting* to have a baby because I thought that wasn't very feminist of me. My understanding of feminism has evolved since then, and now I know that's not true.

I am now getting to that age in life when people are asking when my partner and I will have kids. 'NOT NOW DEAR GOD NO THANK YOU' is my stock answer. But what about if you know you don't want kids? Questions like that can be frustrating and irritating at best, offensive at worst. Society is getting better at respecting a womb-bearer's desire not to procreate, but there's a way to go yet. There is still an underlying expectation of women to conform to traditional 'life stages'. Get an education, get a job, get married, have babies, retire. That life cycle is fed to us from all angles, making it hard for us to say, 'I don't want that. That's not what will make me happy.'

We've been bombarded by the idea of our bodies' 'biological clocks'. While it's true that becoming pregnant gets more difficult and more risky as you get older, is it really the case that at some point our bodies communicate to us, *I must have a baby*? Some people say they genuinely felt a bodily urge to have kids, but arguing that this is a universal experience diminishes the very real and valid choices of people not to have children. Perhaps you don't feel broody at all and then you hit 32 and are like 'Put a baby in me now!' Or you never feel broody and don't have kids by choice, or you never feel broody and do have kids by choice because it's something you've thought about hard and weighed up the pros and cons of. No matter what you choose, your lifestyle and the future you see for yourself is valid.

I am unashamed to admit that I have a baby-crazy mind; even in my mid-twenties, I'm extremely broody. But like I said, I've never actually been pregnant or had a child, so what do I know? Every time I've spoken to a mother or a pregnant person, they always say, 'They never tell you about it, but this thing happened to me' or 'You're never warned about this.' There is just so much going on in a pregnant body!

Dear bump,

You definitely know how to make a girl feel good about herself. Apparently, pregnancy is the only time it's socially acceptable for people to tell you you're getting bigger (or that you're bigger than you should be at this stage — I'm looking at you, dog-groomer!). Thank you for making me weep uncontrollably at episodes of Corrie and old Westlife songs, whilst at the same time making me want to punch someone in the face, cuddle them and give them a health and safety lecture.

Only 22 weeks left of blaming everything on baby brain ...

Sally, UK

Interesting combo.

So we can't talk about hormones without going into one of the biggest hormone changes a body can go through (other than maybe puberty, HRT or menopause) – it's time to dive into pregnancy.

GETTING PREGNANT

We've talked a lot about trying *not* to get pregnant, but one day you may find yourself trying desperately for the opposite to happen. My mum became pregnant with me very soon after coming off contraception, but for others it can take much longer. According to the NHS, most couples of child-bearing age (about 84 per cent) will get pregnant within a year if they have regular sex and don't use contraception. But this varies depending on age. You are more likely to conceive in your early twenties than you are in your late thirties.

Because you never know how long it'll take to get pregnant, it may be best to stop using your method of contraception or have it removed by a professional as soon as you decide you want to try for kids. And, obviously, now you can use fertility awareness methods and apps for the purpose of getting pregnant rather than to avoid it. Instead of avoiding sex in your fertile window, you want to have as much sex as possible! You can even get ovulation tests to track when you release an egg – but remember, you're fertile for five to seven days *before* you ovulate because the sperm can stay alive inside the uterus just waiting for that sweet, sweet egg to be released.

Fertility problems affect one in seven couples. If you've been trying to get pregnant without success for one to two years, then go see your doctor for help. There is treatment available and there are three main types: medication, surgery and assisted conception, such as IVF. Causes of fertility problems will vary from person to person and couple to couple so see your GP for the appropriate course of action. A couple that I watch on YouTube are trying for another baby and they've had fertility issues before so they're making videos and being really open about the IVF process. It's so refreshing to see the way they talk about it so candidly and I imagine their openness is helping a lot of people.

Unlike what you may have heard, you do not get pregnant right after having sex. It may take from a few hours to several days for the sperm and egg to find each other (conception), and then after that it may take several more days for the fertilised egg to implant in the uterine lining. *Et voilà* – you're preggers!

THE STAGES OF PREGNANCY

Pregnancy usually lasts 40 weeks, and as someone who's not experienced pregnancy, I'm like *What are weeks? How many months is that?* Pregnant people and doctors, nurses and midwives speak in this other language of weeks, which the rest of us don't understand because we were always taught that a baby takes nine months to brew. Well, that's not right because I did the maths and considering most months are a little over four weeks, nine months is actually about 38 weeks. And then you have to consider that a 40-week due date is an estimation based on the start of your last period (and you very likely conceived about two weeks after that, when you ovulated) and so a full-term pregnancy is more likely to be around 36 to 40 weeks or something. It's hard to be precise because babies come early and late all the time.

Now we've properly established I know practically nothing about pregnancy, let me tell you about the stages of pregnancy.

The first trimester

This is the first 12 weeks (translation: about three months). The baby cells at this stage are referred to as an embryo – until about eight weeks, when the baby is called a foetus and it's about 2.5 cm long. By week 12, the foetus is the size of a lime.

From what I've gathered, the first trimester can be a challenging ride! Not only are you potentially having pregnancy symptoms such as morning sickness (although morning sickness can happen any time of day), you're also not *supposed* to tell anyone you're pregnant because this is the most vulnerable time for a foetus.

Dear pregnant body,

I found out I was pregnant at three weeks, with an early pregnancy test. I told a couple of close family members, intending to tell more people at 12 weeks. Everyone had opinions on when I should talk about it. Miscarriage is such a taboo that even close family is shocked when they hear you are sharing your pregnancy news with anyone.

I think that is really unfortunate. I now know how many relatives (at least two so far) had miscarriages and suffered in silence. I wish women were not judged and were left free to decide when they want to talk about their pregnancies. For many, having a clued-in support network can really help.

The first physical symptom to hit me was severe fatigue. On week six, the nausea arrived. Food is ruined. I went from being a low-carb healthy eater to only being able to stomach beige food with zero nutrients. Whoever called it morning sickness was surely never pregnant. It is more like all-day, all-night sickness. It is like living on a boat when you are prone to motion sickness. I have yet to have a craving or a positive feeling about food. On the whole I am happy with you, my pregnant body, but I wish I had known what to expect.

We recently had an early scan. The ultrasound lady asked us not to panic if it takes a while to find the baby, since it is very small. But as soon as the ultrasound landed on my stomach, there it was. Until you see it, it just isn't real! The tiny seven-week-old nugget had an obvious and strong heartbeat. This has really raised my spirits and helped me cope.

Julie, UK

It is often recommended that you shouldn't tell people about your pregnancy until you've reached 12 weeks, because of the risk of miscarriage in the first trimester. However, as Julie so eloquently wrote – it's up to you. You can make the choice of who you tell, how and when. And this is something that only occurred to me recently – if no one knows you're pregnant, then it's harder to tell anyone you've miscarried. You may need time off work to recover but don't know what to tell your colleagues or your boss because they never knew you were pregnant in the first place. People who've had miscarriages should not have to suffer in silence just because someone told us we shouldn't talk about pregnancy until 12 weeks. As Julie said, having a supportive network who know what you're going through can really help.

The second trimester

Weeks 13 to 27 (translation: four to six months). If you chose to keep your pregnancy hush before now, then it is time to tell people because your bump will start showing and there's no hiding that. The sex of the foetus develops around this time and you can find that out at the second scan around 18–21 weeks. Then you might do a big sex reveal extravaganza on the internet either in an Instagram or Facebook post or a YouTube video. This is also when you might start to feel the baby move.

Dear fluid retention,

Watching my toes literally bubble
up one at a time was always a fun
way to spend my evening ... not.

What?!

Would have been great if all that fluid
had just stayed where it was needed:
around the baby! I don't think my legs/
arms/toes had anything extra in them
to protect.

And cravings, thanks for being so chill, I
would happily eat an entire cucumber with
tzatziki any day of the year.

Caitlin, Canada

The third trimester

Weeks 28 to birth (translation: seven months to birth). At this point, you're the biggest you're going to get, possibly huge and you're like, *Hurry up and get out of my body.* You're tired and uncomfortable most of the time. Fun fact: at 33 weeks, the foetus weighs almost the same as a pineapple. I don't know about you, but I do not like the sound of a pineapple coming out of my vagina. No thank you. The good news is your foetus is looking pretty baby-like at this point and you could pop any second. Good luck!

Dear pregnancy,

You are the craziest journey I've ever gone on, and you're still not over yet! I've had twenty weeks of throwing up all day, every day. But also, twenty weeks of feeling my little one wriggle and kick. You've given me aching boobs, hips and thighs, even stretch marks that make my tummy look like tiger bread. But I'm grateful to go through this, and am so amazed at what the human body can do.

Five weeks until I meet you, little one. I'm so excited.

Clara, New Zealand

Dear pregnancy,

Part of me is so glad to be done with you, however, the other part of me misses you. With you, my baby had a safe and cosy place to grow and now he is out in this cold, harsh world. On the other hand, I don't miss the constant trips to the bathroom, not being able to see my own vagina, the mood swings and all of the body aches.

My baby wasn't the only thing you provided to me. WHY DID YOU HAVE TO GIVE ME HAEMORRHOIDS!?

Haemorrhoids or 'piles' are swollen blood vessels found in or around your rectum or anus. I had a haemorrhoid after my surgery and I can tell you it's not pleasant. But I count myself lucky because I was no longer needing to poo through my butthole so it wasn't getting aggravated and eventually went away.

I wouldn't wish that on my worst enemy. You pushed my body to its limits and caused me to be pre-eclamptic and made me have the baby three weeks before he was due. But I know with all of that, I was one of the lucky ones who you didn't completely destroy.

Thank you so much for creating my son, but overall, I don't miss you.

Regards,
Kimberly, USA

Dear postpartum body,

You are beautiful in your own way. All these marks show how strong I was bringing my little girl into this world. So what if you are heavier than you've ever been? My worth isn't defined by a number.

Mae, USA

MISCARRIAGE

According to the NHS, roughly one in eight pregnancies ends in miscarriage – but it could be as many as one in four when people who weren't aware they were pregnant are taken into account. Some people will have more than one miscarriage, but recurrent miscarriages aren't common. To be honest, before writing this book I had no idea miscarriage happened so often. Even though I've seen a lot more openness around miscarriage in recent years, it's still not talked about nearly as often as it should be. You never believe it could happen to you until it does.

A miscarriage is the unplanned loss of a pregnancy, the main signs of which are vaginal bleeding and cramping and pain in your lower abdomen. If you think you might be miscarrying, go to your doctor and they may refer you to a hospital. If it is a miscarriage (because you can get normal bleeding and pain in the early weeks of pregnancy) then you can either wait for the tissue to naturally pass out of you (medication can help with that) or you can have minor surgery to remove it if you don't want to wait the one to two weeks it usually takes.

Dear miscarriage,

I honour those who mourn you and stand strongly by their sides, but I should not be demanded to grieve. I should not be shamed for feeling grateful to my body for ridding myself of something I wasn't ready for. My emotions *surrounding you are not up for debate or discussion.*

Some days I coil away in pain at the memory of you, and some days I smile with gratitude. There is no right way to feel. You've taught me the vast difference of everyone's unique experience.

Stephee, USA

Most miscarriages happen in the first 12 weeks of pregnancy, often before many people know you are pregnant, as we've discussed. So not only does the miscarriage take a toll on you physically and mentally, you have the added burden of figuring out how or if to tell people what you're going through so they can accommodate for your needs.

These things are common, they happen, but there's no taking away from the fact they can be really tough to go through, especially alone. If you have a support network in your life or people you can talk to, then I encourage you to talk. There are also charities and online groups and forums out there which are dedicated to giving people who have had miscarriages support.

The knowledge that you're not alone and other people have experienced similar struggles to you can be invaluable. I hope some of these stories bring awareness and comfort.

Dear miscarriage,

I want to hate you, but I can't. I want to be so angry with you, but it won't change anything. You took what I had been hoping for. You robbed me. It's not fair. I want to hate you, but I can't, because that would be replacing the love I had for my baby with hate, and I refuse to give you that power.

Jenah, USA

ABORTION

Dear Ireland,

Yesterday, on 18 September 2018, the president of our country signed the bill to legalise access to abortion after two-thirds of the population voted in favour of the action last summer. Before now, hundreds of Irish women have been forced to travel to Britain every year to access their basic right to adequate healthcare. These women were strong, capable human beings brought to their knees by crisis pregnancies, fatal foetal abnormalities and sexual abuse, and I'm sorry to say this, Ireland, but you turned your back on them.

I have always been lucky enough to have access to judgement-free contraception of my choosing, but I recognise that this is a new-found privilege, and not something to take for granted. Up to now, it has felt like women have had a seat at the table of Irish cultural decision-making, but we've never been given a microphone. By sheer collective mass, we have made our unified voice loud enough to render amplification unnecessary.

Ireland, I take great pleasure in telling you that since I reached the legal voting age, we have become the first country in the world to

Abortion is the planned ending of a pregnancy. One in three women in the UK will have an abortion at some point in her life, which just shows how common abortion is and how important it is that we fight for and protect access to these services. In Great Britain, abortions are available free of charge on the NHS; if you need an abortion or want to discuss your options, you can go to your GP and get a referral, go directly to an abortion provider or go to a sexual-health clinic. Most abortions are carried out before 24 weeks of pregnancy; they are simpler and safer the earlier they are carried out.

Dear antibiotics and my pill,

*I really wish my oral surgeon had reminded me
you don't mix when I got my wisdom teeth taken
out, but she didn't. The resulting pregnancy
and abortion weren't nearly as traumatic as I
initially thought they'd be, but they weren't
exactly fun. When I got an ear infection,
the clinic doctor didn't warn me about your
rivalry either, but I knew better by then.*

I asked him why he didn't mention it, and he said there's such a low chance that doctors don't usually bother.

Ouch.

Sara, Canada

If you're pregnant and you don't want to be, the decision to have an abortion is entirely your own but you may find it easier talking to someone else to support you through the process. If you decide you don't want to tell anyone, your details will be kept confidential even if you're under 16.

There are two types of abortion:

1. The 'abortion pill'

You take two medications 24 to 48 hours apart to induce a miscarriage. In 2018, the British government legalised the taking of the second abortion pill at home in England so you don't have to travel back to the clinic to take it (which for some people is extremely difficult with travel time, money, jobs and family). This was already legal in Wales and Scotland.

2. Surgical abortion

A minor procedure to remove the pregnancy. You can normally go home afterwards.

Dear post-abortion body,

I wish I could have known how much the abortion would affect you. I realised that I would have to struggle with guilt, and possibly regret, but I didn't realise how much you would have to deal with. I put you through a trauma. I made you bleed for months, and sent your hormones completely out of whack. I did not appreciate how much you had to handle, and was impatient with you during recovery.

I promise I will do everything in my power not to put you through that again. And if I get pregnant when we are ready, I will be as patient and loving with you as I can be while we embark on the new adventure. Thank you for putting up with me.

Yours always,
Beth, Belgium

The main message is a simple yet powerful one. It's your body, and what you do with it is your choice. However you feel about the things that happen to your body, that's fine. Your feelings are valid, so live your truth. If you feel grateful for having a miscarriage or terrible after having an abortion, that's fine. There's no proper way to experience these things and you shouldn't feel guilty for not having what you might think is the 'correct' response. No matter how common they are, abortion, miscarriage and pregnancy are all extremely personal, individual experiences. We're all doing our best out here.

Conclusion

So our hormone diaries have taken us the whole way from puberty to pregnancy, but wait. There's one more stop along the road until we can truly, once and for all say goodbye, shut the diary and store it away somewhere: the menopause.

Menopause

For folks who can have babies, there eventually comes a time when you can't have babies: the menopause. I have always found it quite funny how some people put a 'the' in front of menopause. It makes it sound really sinister. Imagine if we did that for puberty. *Now kids, soon you will experience a thing called The Puberty* ... Sounds terrifying!

Menopause happens when our oestrogen levels decline and our ovaries finally close up shop. It occurs between 45 and 55 years of age and in the UK the average age of someone going through menopause is 51. However, some people may experience premature menopause. This affects about one in one hundred people with ovaries.

There are many symptoms associated with menopause, many of them not pleasant. As mentioned in chapter four, there is treatment available in the form of hormone replacement therapy (HRT) that can reduce your symptoms. HRT works by replacing the diminishing oestrogen in your body to make the transition easier.

But I'm not going to tell you about menopausal symptoms, oh no. Another real-life woman who has experienced menopause and lived to tell the tale: my mother!

Lolz. Menopause is not deadly, I feel like I need to clarify that ...!

Dear menopause,

This is the first letter I've written to you and, as such, the first time I've given any real thought to how you have treated me over the last few years. I know for sure that I haven't had a period since I had my coil taken out four years ago. Who knows what my natural cycle would have done in the 15 years of no periods before that? All I do know is that I saved an absolute fortune on sanitary products.

So, menopause – how have you treated me? My gut reaction is pretty damn well. Compared to most of my friends, I have always felt that you let me off lightly. But now I have searched online for menopause symptoms, I'm not so sure. I have put them in order of how much they have bothered me.

1. Hot flushes – These are surges of bodily heat with no forewarning at all. I have even had them in a cool swimming pool! I am lucky with the hot flushes as no one can see how hot and clammy I am actually feeling. Friends of mine suddenly go bright red, visibly sweaty or have to carry a fan with them. An American friend of mine said she refers to hot flushes as power surges. I love that.

2. Night sweats – I had a good few years of waking up soaking wet, getting up and then back to a wet bed, horrible.

3. Difficulty sleeping – When the night sweats were really bad, the sleep was bad too. I do always wake up in the night for a wee and often struggle to get back to sleep. Compared to friends who cannot sleep at all and are exhausted all day, I've got off pretty lightly.

4. *Problems with memory and concentration – OMG this is such a problem. I ask a question a million times because within seconds I've forgotten the answer. I can't remember conversations I've had or people's names. As soon as I've read a book or seen a film, I've forgotten I've even read it or seen it, let alone what it was about. I've been blaming too many drugs when I was younger killing my brain cells or worrying about the onset of dementia ... but now I can blame you!*

5. *Vaginal itchiness and dryness – I had put this down to too much time spent on a saddle cycling ... but it's you!*

6. *Reduced libido – Again, I'd blamed getting older, being more tired, having a busy life ... but it's you!*

7. Joint stiffness, aches and pains
   – Since when did I become that
   person who makes weird grunting
   noises when I get out of the car
   or get up after sitting on the
   floor a while? I was blaming my
   age and my genes (there's a lot
   of arthritis in the family), but
   maybe it's you.

8. Low mood and anxiety – This
   has badly affected some of
   my menopausal friends. These
   things of course affect me, but
   only as part and parcel of an
   average stressful life. I think
   I'll let you off on this one.

9. Weak bones – Well, I did
   break my wrist when I fell
   off my bike last year …
   hopefully not because of you.

I didn't think you'd impacted me that much.
But after writing this, maybe you haven't
treated me quite so well after all.

Debbie Witton, UK

I assume most of my readers are not of menopausal age yet. If you are, maybe you can relate to my mum. If you're not, I encourage you to ask your mother how she's doing. But some women find themselves going through menopause earlier than they might expect. Menopause is considered early if your periods stop before the age of 45, so if you've noticed infrequent periods or them stopping altogether, speak to your GP. Early menopause may occur because the ovaries naturally stop working, or as a result of some cancer treatments or surgery to remove the ovaries. The physical treatment for early menopause is the same as for menopause, but going through it sooner than you expected can be distressing, so do seek help and support if you think you need it.

With the dawning of the menopause, we've come full circle in our hormone journeys. Maybe there's some beautiful metaphor here about the sun rising and setting on our reproductive lives or the circle of life or something. But what I've heard post-menopausal people saying most of the time is, 'Thank fuck that's over'.

BRINGING THE DIARY TO LIFE

We've had a bit of a laugh in this book but also a bit of a cry. It's all well and good saying our bodies are brilliant and we should love them and be proud of them. But sometimes our bodies are against us and the system is against us and we want to scream *LIFE'S NOT FAIR.* We want to understand our bodies and be taught how they work properly as young people so we're not lost and confused adults. We don't want anyone to have to miss school because they can't afford period products. We want more information and research to be done into contraception. We want contraception for folks with penises! We want no stigma around our bodies. We want compassion from our doctors. We want acceptance and rights for trans people and more funding for sexual-health and gender clinics.

It's time to take action. When faced with all of the areas for improvement, we can feel a bit helpless – like we want to change things but don't know how. But if you want to change the hormone diaries of generations to come, then I've got some ideas for you.

Talk

I hope, if anything, this book has encouraged you to talk and to share. Whether that's with your friends, family, teachers or doctors, it is so worth having open conversations about these topics. You could find comfort that you're not alone and someone else is going through or has gone through a similar thing, or you could learn something about how someone else's life is different to yours and understand things from their perspective.

Vote

VOTE – I love the NHS but the reason why we have so many frustrations and bad experiences with it is because it's underfunded. If you're over 18 in the UK, you can vote in elections and you can register to vote from the age of 16. Get on the register and when it's election time, use your vote! Use it to protect our NHS from privatisation. Use it to secure funding for local councils to spend on sexual and reproductive health services. Use it to guarantee rights to trans people. Use your vote. Be heard.

Campaign

Talking is important but if you want to do more, get out and campaign! There are many existing campaigns and charity groups doing amazing work. Join one of those, give your money or your time (or both), or create your own campaign! What are you passionate about? Reproductive rights, period poverty, trans rights, sex education? Make a noise about it.

Become a doctor/scientist/academic

Probably the one that requires the most commitment. Hey, we can even throw 'become an MP' in there. Be the change you want to see and all that! If this topic area is super-interesting to you, have a think about doing it professionally. You could be on the front line of exciting new discoveries and inventions: male contraception and the artificial womb!

This is not the end of my hormone diary. With potential pregnancy and babies and definite menopause in my future, it most certainly is not the end (wooo, can't wait!). I really do hope you've found some comfort in this book, and in all the stories I've shared. Navigating the realm of periods, contraception and hormones is a tricky beast, especially in a world that has universally denied our access to knowledge, resources and rights throughout history. But we get through it by confiding in each other and making the small changes we can. *The Hormone Diaries* is about all of us; and even if you didn't find your exact experience reflected in these pages, that's okay –because you get to keep your own hormone diary. We all do.

Dear diary,

Thanks for the ride.

Love,

Hannah x

ACKNOWLEDGEMENTS

This book was a long time coming and it wouldn't have been possible without the help of many talented, wonderful people.

First, thanks to my parents for encouraging and supporting me to do no work and to rest whilst I was in recovery from my surgeries. I can be a bit of a stressed-out workaholic, so having them tell me I didn't have to write this book until I was ready was seriously invaluable.

Thank you to my editor, Liza, who took the manuscript of word-vomit once I was ready to write and helped me craft it into the book you just read that I am so proud of. Thank you for believing in the message behind this book and believing in me. It was so fun to work with you on this project. Thanks also to Debbie for championing my career as an author with Wren & Rook from *Doing It!* to *The Hormone Diaries* – thanks so much for the incredible opportunity to write and be published!

Big thanks to my manager, James, and my agent, Richard; your patience, kindness and encouragement guaranteed that *The Hormone Diaries* would actually come into existence.

Thank you Becky and Emily, my publicists, for being excellent company at events and all your hard work and belief in me.

Thanks to Laura, who designed the incredible and bold front cover – I'm a big fan of that period blood underwear stain – and Thy for doing an incredible job on the inside design of the book. Thank you Flic for being a marketing whizz and Jane for magically turning a Word document into an actual physical book! And to my love, Dan, thank you for your unwavering love and support and for holding me accountable so I actually wrote the damn thing.

And of course, I can't thank enough not just the people who shared their hormone diaries that ended up in the book, but to *everyone* who commented on my blog, Instagram and YouTube videos sharing their experiences. Thank you for trusting me with your personal stories and I am forever grateful of this supportive, caring and sharing online community. Thank you.

Index

N

O

P

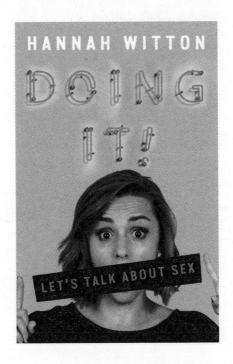

DOING IT!
by Hannah Witton

Sexting. Virginity. Consent. The Big O ... Let's face it, doing it can be tricksy. I don't know anyone (including myself) who has sex all figured out. So I've written a book full of honest, hilarious (and awkward) anecdotes, confessions and revelations. And because none of us have all the answers, I've invited some friends and fellow YouTubers to talk about their sexuality, too.

Paperback 978 1 5263 6003 8 | Ebook 978 1 5263 6004 5
Audio book 978 1 5263 6071 7

YOU GOT THIS
by Bryony Gordon

I have written this book for the teenage girl in me, and for every teenage girl out there. It contains the life lessons I wish someone had taught me. Like don't stress too much about what you'll be when you grow up – as long as you're true to YOU, you'll be fine.

Frank and fearless, *You Got This* openly explores topics like self-respect, body image, masturbation and mental health, making it the perfect companion for young women.

Paperback 978 1 5263 6186 8 | Ebook 978 1 5263 6187 5

CAN EVERYONE PLEASE CALM DOWN?
by Mae Martin

Comedian Mae Martin investigates sexuality in this hilarious and intelligent twenty-first century guide. Covering everything from the pros and cons of labels, to coming out and the joys of sexual fluidity, Mae ponders all the stuff we get hung up about.

Mae's mission is to ensure that in a world that's full of things to worry about, who we choose to kiss is not one of them.

Paperback 978 1 5263 6165 3 | Ebook 978 1 5263 6171 4

RESISTERS
by Lauren Sharkey & Manjit Thapp

Young girls and women are uniting across the world to create change, have their voices heard and stand up for their beliefs.

In this brilliantly inspiring book, Lauren Sharkey profiles the powerful stories and achievements of 52 young campaigners who are working to improve the lives of people across the globe. Some are active in feminist issues like period poverty or political problems such as police brutality. This is a must-have for young women who would dare to make a difference and be the change.

Paperback 978 1 5263 6184 4 | Ebook 978 1 5263 6185 1

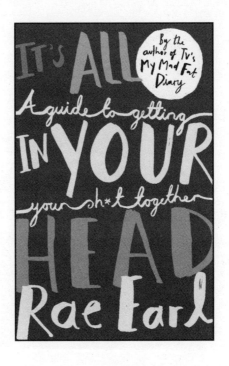

IT'S ALL IN YOUR HEAD

by Rae Earl

As a teenager, I was very adept at hiding my OCD, my anxiety, my depression and my eating disorders behind a smile and a big sack of silly. And that is why I've written this book. Because I hate to think of any teen going through what I did, and feeling like they need to hide it. This is a book to break down taboos, to start conversations, to help you talk about things that seem impossible. You are not alone.

Paperback 978 1 5263 0002 7 | Ebook 978 1 5263 6080 9
Audio book 978 1 5263 6054 0

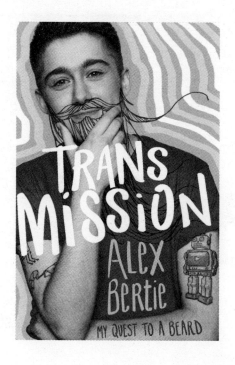

TRANS MISSION
by Alex Bertie

I like pugs, doughnuts and tattoos. I sleep with my socks on. Oh,
and I'm transgender. That's the bit that usually throws people.
Being trans is only one part of who I am, but it's played a huge role
in shaping me. Over the last six years, I've come out to my family,
changed my name, battled the NHS, started taking male hormones
and have had top surgery. My quest to a beard is almost complete.
This is my story.

Paperback 978 1 5263 6068 7 | Ebook 978 1 5263 6068 7
Audio book 978 1 5263 6121 9